THE NEW NATURALIST

A SURVEY OF BRITISH NATURAL HISTORY

THE SEA COAST

The aim of this series is to interest the general reader in the wild life of Britain by recapturing the inquiring spirit of the old naturalists. The Editors believe that the natural pride of the British public in the native flora and fauna, to which must be added concern for their conservation, is best fostered by maintaining a high standard of accuracy combined with clarity of exposition in presenting the results of modern scientific research. The plants and animals are described in relation to their homes and habitats and are portrayed in the full beauty of their natural colours, by the latest methods of colour photography and reproduction.

THE NEW NATURALIST

THE SEA COAST

by

J. A. STEERS

PROFESSOR OF GEOGRAPHY
AND PRESIDENT OF ST. CATHARINE'S COLLEGE
IN THE UNIVERSITY OF CAMBRIDGE

WITH 10 COLOUR PHOTOGRAPHS
TAKEN BY THE AUTHOR
24 PHOTOGRAPHS IN BLACK AND WHITE
52 MAPS AND DIAGRAMS

COLLINS
14 ST. JAMES'S PLACE, LONDON
1953

PLATES IN COLOUR

THE NEW NATURALIST

THE SEA COAST

by

J. A. STEERS

PROFESSOR OF GEOGRAPHY
AND PRESIDENT OF ST. CATHARINE'S COLLEGE
IN THE UNIVERSITY OF CAMBRIDGE

WITH 10 COLOUR PHOTOGRAPHS
TAKEN BY THE AUTHOR
24 PHOTOGRAPHS IN BLACK AND WHITE
52 MAPS AND DIAGRAMS

COLLINS
14 ST. JAMES'S PLACE, LONDON
1953

TO

James and Grace

First published in 1953 by
Collins, 14 St. James's Place, London
Printed by Collins Clear-Type Press
London and Glasgow

ERRATA

The map appearing on page 98 is printed the wrong side up.

Captions to Colour Illustrations 3a and 3b refer to Colour Illustrations 4a and 4b. Captions to Colour Illustrations 4a and 4b refer to Colour Illustrations 3a and 3b.

CONTENTS

PLATES IN COLOUR

PLATES IN BLACK AND WHITE

EDITORS' PREFACE

SOMEWHERE in the heart of the Midlands of England is a spot which can claim to be the most distant in these islands from the sea. Yet the distance from the nearest tide water is less than 70 miles. If the sea is a part of every Briton's natural heritage, then the sea coast is doubly so ; and it must be rare to find an inhabitant of the British Isles of mature years who has never seen the sea. Another volume in the *New Naturalist* series has disclosed the richness of the flora of our coasts and that wealth in plants is due in large measure to the great variety of coastal habitats. The British coasts have indeed everything —from towering cliffs rising several hundred feet sheer from deep water to mud flats a mile or more wide uncovered by every tide; from restless shingle spits and moving sand dunes to granite headlands which see little change in a century. How is it that along some stretches, despite all the efforts of man, the sea succeeds in gnawing away several feet of land a year, only to throw back the discarded material a few miles away? In this book Professor Steers seeks to explain, as far as the present state of knowledge will permit, how the varied types of coastline have been evolved and how the changes still taking place provide such a remarkable range of differing conditions for plant and animal life.

Now Professor of Geography and President of St. Catharine's College, in the University of Cambridge, and previously Dean and Tutor of his College, his special field of study has been the evolution of coasts and coastlines. His studies took him early to the Great Barrier Reefs and to the cays of the West Indies, but these expeditions were but holidays from the long continued detailed studies of the Norfolk coast—resulting in a book devoted exclusively to Scolt Head Island. When the Ministry of Town and Country Planning was set up he was commissioned by the Minister to make a comprehensive survey of the whole coastline of England and Wales. The lengthy report which resulted provides the essential basic information on which policies of coastal preservation and development can be based.

When this was completed Professor Steers undertook a similar survey of Scottish coasts. As a natural consequence he became a member of The Nature Conservancy and so retains a continuing interest in work 'which must of necessity be greatly concerned with the natural history of coastal lands.

Clearly no-one is better qualified to write on the Sea Coast, and in this book we believe he has successfully combined a clear exposition of what we know, with an indication of the many directions in which the amateur observer can help in the elucidation of outstanding problems—in the true tradition of the field naturalist.

THE EDITORS

AUTHOR'S PREFACE

THERE ARE many ways of studying the coast of a country. In this book the approach is physiographical—that is to say a study of coastal scenery in relation to its origin. This is a vast subject, and cannot be treated fully in a volume of this size, nor by one author. The proper understanding of the coast must be the result of the combined research of workers in several subjects—including geography, geology, ecology, and botany. In the meantime it is perhaps worth while for someone to try to give a comprehensive picture and to call attention to some of the ways in which our knowledge of the coast needs augmenting. I can only make two claims to do this; first I love the coast, and secondly it has been my good fortune to see the whole of the mainland coast of Great Britain and by far the greater part of that of the adjacent islands. This experience has emphasized only too clearly how impossible it is for any one person adequately to deal with so big a subject!

In this volume there are three main themes: (1) A brief synopsis of the relation of coast to the structure of the country and a summary analysis of the physical agencies working on the coast; (2) a discussion of the nature of different types of coastal scenery; and (3) a short account of the evolution of parts of our coastline. The final chapter on raised beaches and submerged forests is conveniently treated by itself, but its subject matter is relevant to all the other chapters.

So far as I am aware no one has attempted to deal physiographically and in some detail with the whole coast of Scotland. To do so at this stage would, I think, be difficult, much as the subject deserves it. This is so for several reasons. First of all a great deal more local work is required on specific problems and places. The interesting and extensive dunes of Aberdeenshire are now for the first time being studied. The Machair of the Western Isles, the Ayres of Orkney and the numerous saltmarshes all demand attention. Extremely little has been written about the cliffed coasts of Scotland—a study involving the relation of structure to marine erosion and other factors along miles of interesting and beautiful coast, and presenting problems for many workers. The investigation of raised beaches and associated phenomena has hardly begun in the sense of explaining how they were cut and the human uses to which they are now put. Moreover, the actual sequence is not always quite clear—where, for example, does the " pre-Glacial " beach of Islay, Colonsay, and the Treshnish Isles fit? Perhaps the controvery concerning the origin of fiords is settled, but there is still scope for much work on the local differences in form of the western sea-lochs. Still more important, and this applies to England and Wales with equal force, is the examination and mapping of the topography of the adjacent sea floor. The full study of a coast must depend a great deal on a knowledge of the adjacent submarine floor—and yet how little is this matter discussed in many coastal studies in which its introduction would be highly relevant!

Coastal scenery also depends greatly on that of the country to which it forms the margin. The contrast between the flat-topped cliffs of the Hartland district of North Devon and the hog's-back cliffs of Exmoor; or the striking difference between the even skyline of the cliffs of the Tenby and Gower Peninsulas or of the Lizard district with the coast on either side of Salcombe Harbour in South Devon or with that of the north coast of Sutherland, all demand attention if we are going to explain fully the scenery of our coastline.

I am fully aware of many of the shortcomings of this book, and also of the generalizations made in it. A complete explanation of the intricate landscape of the Western Isles and mainland of Scotland is not at present possible. The origin of the North Sea and its connection with the cliffs of our east coasts, the reason for the Shetland archipelago, the former river systems of the North Channel and Irish Sea, the significance of the Cornubian peninsula, and the means of separation of Britain from the Continent and of Ireland from Britain are all great and largely unsolved problems. Yet to appreciate our coastline fully we must try to understand these topics just as much as the more obvious ones of erosion and accretion. If I have done nothing else than provoke discussion or disagreement I am well satisfied because it has always seemed to me that some of these matters have been all too readily overlooked—and it is a long time since Sir Halford Mackinder introduced some of them in his *Britain and the British Seas*.

Once again I acknowledge with great pleasure my indebtedness to Dr. H. Dighton Thomas, who read through this book in typescript

and made many helpful suggestions. To the Editors of the New
Naturalist volumes I am also grateful for much constructive help
and criticism. The diagrams have nearly all been drawn for me by
Mr. L. R. Thurston, who spent much time and care on them. The
sources of those diagrams based on the work of others are all duly
acknowledged elsewhere. Permission to use maps and diagrams which
have appeared in official publications has been obtained from the
H.M. Stationery Office. The Royal Geographical Society and the
Cambridge University Press have also kindly allowed me to make use
of certain maps and figures. The photographs are from various
sources, and I am indeed glad to record my thanks to those who have
allowed me to make use of them. The origin of each photograph
is given below it.

In order that the large figures 44, 47 and 50 (pp. 204, 220 and
236) may be printed from single blocks, they have had to be placed
somewhat remotely from the text-passages to which they refer.

The Index was compiled by Mr. Geoffrey Willett, to whom I am
most grateful.

J. A. Steers,
Cambridge, May, 1952

*It should be noted that throughout this book Plate numbers in arabic figures
refer to the Colour Plates, while roman numerals are used for Black-and-
White Plates*

CHAPTER I

THE RELATION OF THE COAST
TO THE GENERAL STRUCTURE
OF GREAT BRITAIN

BEFORE discussing coastal matters *sensu stricto*, it will repay us to glance at the general relation between the structure of the rocks forming the coastline of Great Britain and that of the country as a whole (Fig. 1, p. 4).

Although the interpretation of much of the geology of Scotland is still hypothetical, the main structural regions of the country are clearly differentiated, and are associated with coastlines possessing marked characteristics. The dominant grain of Scotland is north-east and south-west over most of the country, but more nearly north-north-east and south-south-west in the North-west Highlands. To this geological fact must be added the physical one—namely, that Scotland is higher in the west than in the east. The slope of the country to the east and south-east is related to the preservation of the Old Red Sandstone in Caithness and around the Moray Firth. Formerly this formation, as well as still newer ones, spread over some of the mountainous interior.

The effect of the grain on the coastline is apparent in many places, but from Cape Wrath to the Caithness border, along the Moray Firth particularly in Banffshire, in Argyll, Jura, Islay, and Kintyre, it is conspicuous. This is emphasised in Figs. 20 and 21, pp. 90, 93 which illustrate how the headlands and re-entrants of Sutherland and Banff follow the trend of the rocks which form them. In Argyll and the adjacent islands the correspondence is often more obvious, but is best appreciated by a study of a geological map of the whole country.

Whilst the folds and thrusts, which enter so largely into the structure of the North-west Highlands, are generally parallel to the coastline, it is nevertheless the case that the north-west and south-east trends of sea lochs, valleys, and igneous dykes, produce the most effective coastal scenery in western Sutherland and Wester Ross.

The gradual change from the north-west and south-east trend of the sea lochs between Cape Wrath and Skye, through the east and west direction of those between the Kyle of Lochalsh and Loch Sunart, and then to the south-westerly trend of the Great Glen and the Argyll lochs, hardly reflects the major structural traits of the country, which are more clearly shown in the parallelism of the Outer Hebrides and the North-west Highlands, and that of the Coll-Tiree ridge with the prevailing grain of the Grampians. The region from the Shiant islands to the south of Mull was at one time buried under lavas and other products of the great volcanoes of Skye, Rum, Ardnamurchan, and Mull. This and the later collapse of parts of the area obscure the relations between the coastline and the general structure of the country.

In the Central Valley, between the great faults bordering the Highlands and the Southern Uplands, a tract of country, the rocks of which have been folded in a south-west and north-east pattern, has been dropped down. This general direction of strike of the strata as shown on a map is clearest in the Old Red Sandstone outcrop extending from Loch Lomond to Stonehaven, but it is also apparent in the trends of the Ochil and Sidlaw Hills, and in the folds involving the Carboniferous strata. The trend, however, has no very pronounced effects on the coast except perhaps between Stonehaven and Arbroath. In the Firths of Tay and Forth, and also inland, numerous outcrops of igneous rock and the necks of old volcanoes are more likely to focus the attention, than is the influence on scenery of the strike of the beds in which they are intruded.

The marked trend of the Southern Uplands locally affects the coast, especially near St. Abb's Head and in Wigtownshire. It may also be observed *in detail* on parts of the Solway coast,[1] and in the line of the Solway Firth. The bays and larger inlets of Wigtown, Kirkcudbright, and Dumfries are discordant, and may recall a time when rivers flowed on a cover of newer rocks and so passed athwart the grain of the older rocks.

The cartographical relation between the major structural trends

[1] *Mems. Geol. Surv.*, Scotland, Sheet 5, Kirkcudbrightshire; J. Horne *et al* 1896. " So rapid are the folds that upwards of sixty anticlines and synclines have been mapped between Corsegard Point and Knockbrex, a distance of one and a quarter miles."

of the country and the coast is close enough, but the field relationships are often obscured; along many miles of the Moray Firth and of Aberdeenshire sand flats and wide dune systems hide it completely. Elsewhere, the frequent raised beaches and the grassing over of the old cliffs may divert attention from it. Yet in the trend of small inlets, the lines of cliff faces, the direction of certain valleys, and in all sorts of other ways, the grain has a pervasive effect. In places, not only cliff detail but also that of the adjoining land, may be completely hidden by boulder clay. This, however, is a more marked characteristic of coasts south of the Border.

In England and Wales the relation of coast to the structure of the interior of the country is perhaps less impressive. Geological maps emphasise the strike of the Jurassic and Cretaceous beds, and the scarps of the Cotswolds and Chiltern Hills, but in eastern England the influence of either the trend or of the rocks composing these formations is small indeed. In the coastal parts of Holderness and Lincolnshire the Cretaceous beds are completely hidden by boulder clay, and in north Norfolk, apart from an outcrop at Hunstanton, the Chalk lies behind a wide fringe of salt marsh, and only makes a final appearance on the foreshore at and near Sheringham.

From the Border to Flamborough Head, rock type locally has a great effect on the coastal scenery (see page 201), although the connection between the coastal scenery and the structure of both coast and interior is not striking. On the coast itself this is partly because the extensive sandy beaches and long lines of dunes on the Northumberland coast hide it. The Carboniferous rocks of Northumberland and Durham are roughly concentric around The Cheviot, and for many miles south of Berwick they (including the Calciferous sandstone series) outcrop on the coast in such a way as to give rapidly alternating beds of usually thin sandstones, shales, and limestones locally intruded by the Whin Sill, which produces the most interesting features, including the Farne Islands. The Millstone Grit and Coal Measures follow to the south, and form the coastline of the southern part of Northumberland. The Magnesian limestone, of Permian age, makes nearly the whole of the Durham coast.

In the Cleveland district of Yorkshire, the Jurassic rocks are gently folded along an east and west axis, but near the coast, local anticlines and synclines modify the major trend. The low ground near the Tees mouth is clearly related to the soft Permian and Triassic rocks thereabouts.

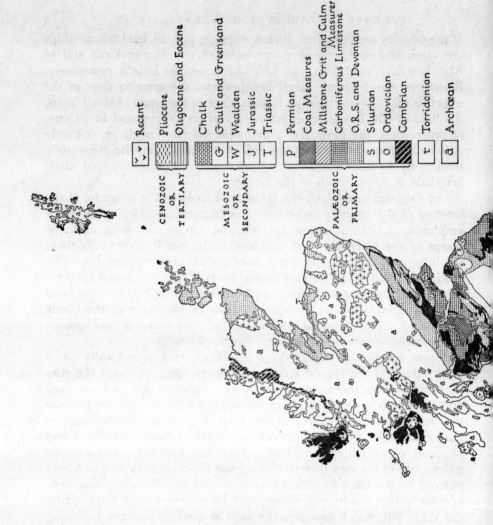

	Recent	v v	CENOZOIC OR TERTIARY
	Pliocene		
	Oligocene and Eocene		
	Chalk		MESOZOIC OR SECONDARY
	Gault and Greensand	G	
	Wealden	W	
	Jurassic	J	
	Triassic	T	
	Permian	P	PALEOZOIC OR PRIMARY
	Coal Measures		
	Millstone Grit and Culm Measure		
	Carboniferous Limestone		
	O.R.S. and Devonian		
	Silurian	S	
	Ordovician	O	
	Cambrian		
	Torridonian	t	
	Archæan	a	

Volcanic rocks of various ages

Granites and other intrusive rocks of various ages

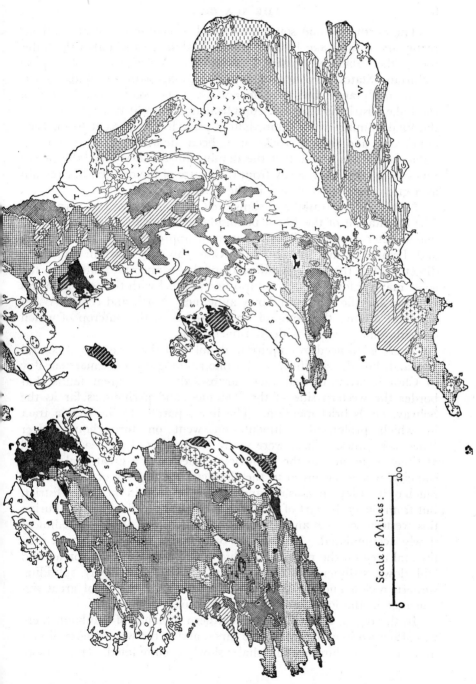

Scale of Miles:

100

0

FIG. 1—A simplified Geological map of the British Isles. (Based on Geological Survey.)

The north-east and south-west trend so characteristic of Scotland reappears in the Lake District and in Wales. In the Lakes the older rocks—the Skiddaw Slates, Borrowdale Volcanics, and Upper (Silurian) Slates—are approximately parallel with the folds in the Southern Uplands, but they do not reach the coast. The history of the Lake District is long and complicated; suffice it to say that before the final doming which immediately preceded its present form, Carboniferous and newer rocks had been deposited over the older Palaeozoics. As a result of the doming in Tertiary time, the newer rocks have been worn away from the centre of the district, but remain as a girdle on the coast and in the Eden valley.

North and central Wales show the Caledonian trend to advantage. The orientation of the Lleyn peninsula conforms to it, as also do the major outcrops in Anglesey. Between, approximately, Aberystwyth and Pembrokeshire, the coast of Cardigan Bay runs in the same direction, but the exact significance of this is uncertain, although the coast may conform to a structural line parallel with the central Wales syncline and the Teifi and Towy anticlines. North and central Wales are built around the dome of Cambrian rocks, the outcrop of which coincides fairly closely with Merionethshire.

There is no need to enquire in detail into the structure of central England, but the significance of a line running from Carmarthen Bay to Church Stretton, and then northwards to the great faults that border the western side of the Pennines, and perhaps as far as the Solway, needs brief mention. The line separates to the west a tract in which prolonged sedimentation went on throughout Lower Palaeozoic times. There were many movements of the sea floor, and at times, especially in the Ordovician, there was a great deal of vulcanicity, which has given us the characteristic scenery of Cader Idris, much of the Lleyn peninsula, and the Borrowdales in the Lake District. But from the early part of the Cambrian until the close of the Silurian this western sea was an area in which thousands of feet of sediment slowly accumulated. To the east of this long line there was a continental area on the margins of which the sea occasionally spread and laid down sediments. The contrast between the slowly subsiding western region and the continental areas to the east is of great significance in the formation of the Caledonian mountains.

In the region now called the Southern Uplands of Scotland, there was also a sea in early Palaeozoic times, and in the waters more distant from the coast, thin and fine shales slowly accumulated. In the more coastal parts, sedimentation was far more rapid. A comparison of the rocks in the Hawick and Girvan districts soon reveals the difference of conditions.

In the North-west Highlands region there was also an early Palaeozoic sea. The Cambrian rocks of that area were deposited in it, but its later history is obscure.

In all three regions there was great tectonic activity at the close of Silurian times. For whatever may have been the reason, the sediments which had accumulated in the seas were violently squeezed and folded, and later raised into mountain ranges. The details vary from place to place, but the general direction of movement was from the south-east, and it is this which has produced the marked north-east and south-west grain so noticeable in these regions of Caledonian folding.

In South Wales and in southern England the trend of the rocks is more nearly east and west. This is exemplified with great clarity in the coalfield of South Wales, and the adjacent folding in the Tenby and Gower peninsulas. It occurs in the Mendips, and in Cornwall and Devon. Farther east it gives rise to the characteristic scenery of the Isles of Purbeck and Wight, and of the Weald. The main direction of the syncline of the London Basin is in accord, and so also is that of the lower Bristol Channel.

The east-west trend in the south of Britain is the result of folding movements of two distinct and long separated periods of time. The folding of the coalfield and adjacent parts of South Wales took place at the end of Carboniferous times, and is named the Armorican folding. The much newer folding of the Tertiary period, the Alpine folding, followed the same east and west direction, but also involved much newer rocks. In Kent the surface folding, which is the key to so much of the scenery, is generally parallel to the underlying folds which have been studied in the deeply buried Kent coalfield. This ancient folding is probably continuous below the surface with that of South Wales on the one side, and the Boulonnais, Belgian coalfield, and the Ruhr on the other.

The Armorican and Alpine folds are largely responsible for the major pattern of our southern coasts. The Chalk headlands of the North and South Forelands, and Beachy Head, the sweeping curves in the softer Wealden and Tertiary beds of the Hampshire basin, the lozenge-shape of the Isle of Wight, the intricate relation of structure and coastal scenery in Purbeck, the disposition of the rocks in Cornwall

CHAPTER 2

THE MOVEMENTS OF BEACH MATERIAL

THE MOST casual acquaintance with the coast of this country reveals the fact that lines of cliff and beach, capes and headlands standing out into deep water, bays with sandy beaches, and large expanses of shingle are common and repeated features.

In the first place it is important to realise that beaches are not permanent. That this is so is perhaps best seen during a storm which may remove the whole of a particular beach. If the place where it formerly stood is then examined it will be realised that the materials composing the beach rest on a platform cut in whatever rock may be present. Sometimes, in more sheltered places, the sands and gravels may rest on a slope or ledge of rock hardly if at all modified by marine action, but in the more open or exposed localities the platform under the beach is an erosion product. Beaches may also have the form off-shore bars (*q.v.*).

The sands, gravels, and coarser materials making the beaches are primarily formed by the erosion of some pre-existing rocks. It may be that the cutting of the platform itself is the main source of the material resting on it. Frequently, however, the beach material of a particular locality has migrated to that place from elsewhere. Let us see, therefore, how material moves alongshore. There are two main ways: by beach drifting and by currents, and each needs careful attention.

On an open beach it is often noticeable that waves do not break directly parallel with the trend of the coast, but approach at an oblique angle. If their action is watched, it is plain that as the wave breaks it sends rushing obliquely up the beach a mass of water called the swash or send. This water carries stones and smaller material with it, which move up the beach in the same direction as the swash. Where the swash dies away, the water that has not percolated down-

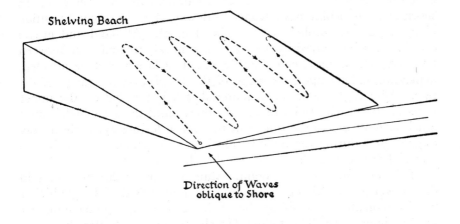

Shelving Beach

Direction of Waves
oblique to Shore

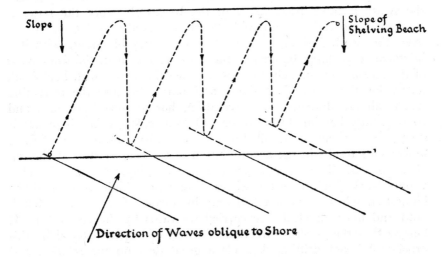

Slope

Slope of
Shelving Beach

Direction of Waves oblique to Shore

Fig. 2

Diagrams showing the drift of shingle along a shelving beach

TABLE 1

SCOLT HEAD ISLAND

Date 1933	Direction of movement of pebbles stones	Average daily movement of pebbles	Maximum movement	Wind Direction	Wind Average velocity	General direction from which waves approached beach	Remarks
July 4	W.	laid down	0 yds.	N.E.	c. 10 m.p.h.	N.	From 4–14 July waves small, rather large on 15 and 16 July.
„ 5	E.	3–4 yds.	40 yds. W.	E.N.E.	c. 8–9 m.p.h.	N.N.E.	
„ 6	—	⅔ yd.	14 yds. W.	E.N.E.	c. 3–4 m.p.h.	N-N.N.E.	
„ 7	W.	—	—	S.E.-S.W.	c. 18 m.p.h.	N-N.N.E.	July 7–11 the direction of movement rather anomalous.
„ 8	W.	6–7 yds.	41 yds. W.	S.W.	c. 10 m.p.h.	N.N.W.	
„ 9	—	3 yds.	46 yds. W.	S.W.	c. 5–7 m.p.h.	N.N.W.	
„ 10	W.	2 yds.	72 yds. W.	S.W.	c. 15 m.p.h.	N.N.W.	
„ 11	E.	2 yds.	42 yds. W.	S.W.	c. 15-12 m.p.h.	N.N.W.	
„ 12				S.W.	c. 5 m.p.h.	N.N.W.	
„ 13	E.	5 yds.	8 yds. E.	S.W.	c. 10 m.p.h.	N.N.W.	New series of observations commenced 13 July as earlier pebbles all left above high-water mark.
„ 14	E.	2 yds.	12 yds. E.	S.W.	c. 10-15 m.p.h.	N.N.W.,-N.N.E.	
„ 15	E.	1 yd.	12 yds. E.	S.W.-N.E.	c. 15 m.p.h.	N.N.W.,-N.N.E.	
„ 16	E.	1 yd.	13 yds. E.	N.	c. 15 m.p.h.	N.	

Figure 3, and the downward loss of power is rapid.[1] On the bottom there may be only a to-and-fro motion. A rough but useful test of what happens on a sandy foreshore can easily be made when bathing. If you stand in water about four or five feet deep when ordinary calm weather waves are running, you will find that as the wave passes you, you are lifted up a little. At the same time (Fig. 3) you are " bent " shorewards when the crest passes, and in the opposite direction during the passage of the trough. The general effect is visible when a wind is blowing over a field of corn in ear. The whole field appears as if it were waving, but any individual stalk and ear is not displaced in the sense of being torn out of the ground, but the ear of wheat undergoes a motion something like the water particles in a wave. A similar kind of motion applies to you if you stand firm when you are bathing. At the same time you may notice that the lighter sand is stirred up around your feet.

If you allow yourself to float, and let the water take you as it will,

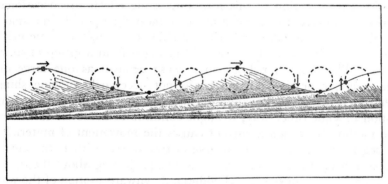

FIG. 3 Wave motion

you may be carried along, slowly, but roughly parallel with the beach. It is the tidal current which is doing this, and these currents vary in direction with the state of the tide. At any given locality they can be investigated, but on an open beach it may happen that with a rising tide the movement is, say, eastward, whereas on a falling tide it is in the opposite direction. If you continue your observations while bathing, and if you peer down a little under the water, you will note

[1] Approximately the relation between the movement of the particles and the depth is: " If L is the length of the wave, the movement of the particles from the surface downwards decreases one half for each 1/9 L of depth; i.e., at a depth of 1/9 L the movement is 1/2 that at the surface; at 2/9 L it is 1/4 the movement at the surface, etc." (R. S. Patton and H. A. Marmer, The Waves of the Sea, in Physics of the Earth; V, Oceanography, Bull. Nat. Res. Council, Washington, 1932.)

is weaker because the swash has spread over a bigger area, and has therefore lost more by percolation; also the greater amount of friction lessens the effect of the backwash. The length of constructive waves is greater than that of destructive waves. The nearly vertical plunge of a destructive wave is induced by the great mass of water brought to the beach by its predecessor, thus allowing the new wave to travel farther inshore, and plunge vertically on to a stretch of water without any extensive swash. These factors intensify the backwash. In a constructive wave, the orbital motion is more elliptical, and Lewis thinks that they break at an earlier stage in their orbit than do destructive waves (Fig. 4).

The action of waves on beaches needs much more attention, but certain generalisations may be made, although future work may lead to some modification of them. It is often noted after storms or strong onshore winds that beaches have been combed down and their profile flattened. In normal and calm weather, the profile is steepened. Storm waves are more likely to result from gales near to, or not far distant from, the shore, and are not to be confused with a ground-swell, the product of a distant gale. Storm waves are high in proportion to their length and so they may resemble destructive waves. There are, however, still many uncertainties. Big storm waves, although they comb down a beach, also throw up shingle to its highest parts, or even over its crest, and big swell waves may have a destructive effect because friction and percolation will then have less relative effect in weakening the great volumes of swash and backwash, and the effect of gravity may thus make the backwash dominant.

Further complications arise because two or even more sets of waves may approach a beach at the same time, or because smaller waves may be superimposed on larger ones. There is much scope for intelligent observation of the effect of waves on beaches, and anyone staying by the sea can contribute to the solution of the problem if he will note carefully the weather conditions, especially the strength and direction of the wind, the height and general appearance of the waves, the rate at which they break (i.e. so many per minute), and, as far as possible, the effect they are having on the beach. Any simple statement of the matter is impossible. Destructive waves may begin to work on a beach profile built up by constructive waves, or *vice versa*, or perhaps a swell may run in and break upon a beach formed by storm waves, or possibly some peculiar local conditions may exist. However, the effects of waves on beaches may be watched and can often be measured, so that any carefully made series of observations is of value.

Some of our beaches do not run parallel with the general trend of the coast, but turn at a slight angle from it, so that they align themselves rather more perpendicularly to the main waves which break upon them.[1] Blakeney Point, for example, turns outwards from the coast and runs to the north of west for most of its length; the bends in Hurst Castle spit at the mouth of the Solent may be similarly related to the winds and waves playing on it. In Cardigan Bay, Morfa Dyffryn and Morfa Harlech turn away from the trend of coast, and their seaward sides are orientated approximately at right angles to the dominant winds (Fig. 27, p. 123). The same phenomenon may be traced in numerous other examples. If the prevalent and dominant winds are from the same, or nearly the same, direction, conditions are fairly simple, but if the prevalent winds and waves come in from a different quarter from that of the dominant ones, complexities arise. The speed and direction of beach-drifting may become variable, and often much extra material is added to the foreshore of the growing spit or beach.

Beaches, then, are constructed features, and the part above water is wholly the result of wave action, although currents may affect the lower part. They may form at the foot of cliffs, and may fringe the coast for many miles. In more indented shores, beaches are common at the head of bays and gulfs, for example, Mount's Bay, St. Bride's Bay, the Duddon Estuary, Holborn Bay and Sinclair's Bay in Caithness, and in the numerous smaller inlets and coves on the coasts of Pembrokeshire, Cornwall, and Devon. In the north of Scotland there are some excellent examples, including Sandwood Bay, Torrisdale Bay, and Farr Bay. But around the exposed coast between many of these re-entrants there is often no beach at all. The material worn from the cliffs, or sometimes that which has travelled from a greater distance, is swept up the inlet and gathers as a beach. Since the upper parts of narrow gulfs are generally sheltered, the beach need not necessarily rest on a platform of erosion, but may merely gather in the shallow head waters. Sometimes it is partly built of fluviatile deposits if a brook flows into the inlet.

Beaches in a gulf or loch may form not at the head, but at some intermediate point and run out athwart its course. There are some excellent examples in south-west Ireland; one of the best examples in Great Britain occurs at the mouth of Inverness Firth (Fig. 33), where Ardersier Point and Chanonry Point have grown outwards and

[1] W. V. Lewis, *Proc. Geol. Assoc.*, 49, 1938, 107.

almost towards one another from opposite banks. In Cemlyn Bay, in Anglesey, there is a good example of a bay bar which has impounded a tidal lagoon.

Much of the sand and other material that forms a beach is obtained from the sea floor. Waves break in water the depth of which is approximately half the wave length. In stormy weather when big waves are running, the sea floor may be churned up well offshore, and if it consists of suitable material can afford a great supply of detritus. It is difficult, for example, to account for the apparent renewal of the beaches in places like Scolt Head Island unless the new matter is assumed to come from the sea floor which was at one time covered, at least in part, with boulder clay. That beaches can be formed wholly from offshore material in this way is clearly proved in parts of Scotland. Near Claigan on Loch Dunvegan (Skye) there are two unusual beaches formed of the glistening white remains of lime-secreting organisms which live on the adjacent sea bed. Since the fragments have some resemblance to broken coral, the beaches are often called coral beaches. Whilst this is not correct, the name serves to distinguish these beaches from those formed of sand and gravel. The corallines, when they break up, produce great quantities of a coarse calcareous sand, which is spread over the sea bed and eventually washed up to make the beaches.[1]

When the sea bed deepens gradually, it often happens that except in calm weather waves break some way beyond low-water mark of ordinary tides. These waves erode the sea floor where they break, and may throw some of the eroded material up on to the uneroded part in front. If this process is continued, a ridge or bar of sand, shell, and perhaps shingle may be built. It is called an offshore bar. In the early stages of its evolution it is likely to change form rapidly, or to be washed away only to be built again later on. Once, however, it attains a reasonable degree of stability it will, in course of time, be pushed up above the zone of normal wave-break. At low water much of its seaward side may be exposed, and under favourable conditions the wind may carry sand to the bar. Sooner or later seeds reach it, take root and produce tufts of grass. Once this has happened further growth of the bar is much more likely. Perhaps the original bar may

---

[1] See D. Haldane, *Trans. Edin. Geol. Soc.* 13, 1931-38, 442. The nullipore is a robust form of *Lithothamnium calcareum*, Aresch, and at low tide can be seen growing on the spit connecting Lampay Island with the shore. Nullipore sands also occur at Loch Bracadale, Morar, Arran, Lower Loch Fyne, South Bute, and Cumbrae.

become a continuous dune ridge. It is likely that Scolt Head Island and several other similar features originated in this way (Fig. 22, p. 98).

Once a beach has formed either alongside a cliff or as an offshore bar, or in any other locality where there is room for it to develop, it will probably extend one way or the other as a result of beach-drifting. This process is important, not only physiographically, but economically since it largely accounts for the sanding or silting up of many harbours. The general effects are seen in many places, but in few are they better exemplified than in Sussex and Suffolk. The Arun, Adur, Ouse, and Cuckmere, are all deflected eastward by shingle ridges. In Suffolk, Orford Ness, and the smaller spits at the mouths of the Deben and Orwell are of the same nature. Spits grow rather like an embankment or tip heap. Beach-drifting gradually sweeps material along them and, at their ends, adds to the dump. Since the process is fairly continuous, it follows that the accumulated deposits may be conspicuous. On the other hand a spit growing out in this way across a river mouth, or across a bay or other re-entrant in the coast is easily attacked by the waves, especially those that approach it from a direction contrary to that of its growth. For this reason the free end of the growing spit is often turned or bent inwards, and in rather more severe weather large parts of it may be completely cut off.

Changes of this kind are common, but we do not know the precise causes. We know that in a certain storm such and such a spit was shortened, and we may make a shrewd guess as to what may have happened. But precisely what happened and why is quite another matter. Similarly, it is a well-known fact that many sand and shingle beaches, but especially shingle ones, are not merely a simple line of stones, but have running back from them branch ridges called laterals, or recurved ends. Figs. 25 and 26, (pp. 104, 107) show this. Each lateral ridge was at one time the distal or free end of the growing spit. Later, for some reason or other, conditions caused the main beach to lengthen again, and to continue to do so until another lateral was formed. Figures 25 and 26 show that the laterals often meet the main ridge at high angles, even at right angles. The newer laterals, especially those we may see forming over a period of years, may bend gently round. Hence, something has happened to bring about the abrupt junction of the older laterals with the main ridge. The main beach has been over-rolled on to them as is indicated in Fig. 24, p. 103. A direct proof of this inrolling can sometimes be found if marsh deposits are exposed on the foreshore. These deposits can often be shown to have originated

C

inside the spit, which because of the occasional overtopping by big waves has been rolled landwards. A misleading impression of stability is given if the main ridge is now dune covered.

In another chapter some of the coastal districts in which these lateral ridges are well developed are analysed. In this, it is emphasised that each such ridge was built by wave action, and was therefore at one time the outer ridge, and it follows that if one ridge lies in front of, or cuts across another, it is the newer one. Thus by carefully mapping the ridges, and noting their relationships one with another, the evolution of the whole structure of a shingle foreland may be investigated. Difficulties occur, especially in places where the ridges are in groups, but the groups themselves separated from one another. It is, for example, far from clear just how the several groups which are truncated by the present beach ridge on the southward facing part of Dungeness are related to one another and to the formation of the whole foreland. Reconstructions that have been made are quite possible, even probable, but they remain hypothetical (see page 162).

CHAPTER 3

EROSION AND ACCRETION:
EVIDENCE OF COASTAL CHANGES

IN OTHER parts of this book there are references to recent changes in the coast, to erosion and deposition. In this chapter an attempt is made to try to bring together various lines of thought to show the close interlocking between physiographical studies of the coast, archaeology, and history.

It is logical to work from early times up to the present, but that approach may be dangerous, since accounts of early changes are often based on too few facts but on considerable imagination. Changes today are taking place mainly by erosion or by deposition; the slow vertical movement of the land surface suspected in south-eastern England may be very important in the long run, but need not be discussed at the moment (see, however, page 268).

Consider first the question of the rate of erosion of cliffs. Erosion to some extent is taking place in many parts of our coasts, but it is most marked in softer rocks or where for some reason the structure of the cliffs favours it. (See Chapter 5.) The most spectacular example is the Holderness coast of Yorkshire. Recent analysis suggests there are three main factors associated with this erosion.[1] From Bridlington as far as Barmston the *cliff* was not suffering in 1947, but it was thought that a good deal of erosion was taking place on the sea floor for one or two miles outwards from the beach. The water is heavily charged with clay, and the staining thus produced extends in long tongues to the south-east. On the other hand between 1840 and 1890 erosion along this line of cliffs was severe. From Barmston to Spurn Head

---

[1] For recent information on Holderness I have made considerable use of an unpublished report, 7 July 1947, by G. M. Hines and C. Pinsent, Research officers to the Ministry of Town and Country Planning (Leeds), and shown to me by the kindness of the Regional Controller.

erosion is serious, and averages two to three yards a year, and in places a rate of five yards over a period of years has been reached. Most of the pill-boxes erected on the cliffs during the 1939–1945 war are now half submerged in the beach sands. Houses have been wrecked by the collapse of the promenade at Withernsea, and at Skipsea a farm building, which in 1945 was slightly damaged at one end by cliff falls, was in 1947 derelict, half of its 45 feet of length having disappeared.

In Holderness, as often elsewhere, much of the erosion is attributed to the drainage of land water. Springs from interbedded gravels and water from land drains cut deep gullies in the cliffs. Other reasons, apart from the direct attack of the waves, include the loosely compacted nature of much of the boulder clay in the cliffs, the action of frost in cracks, the low equilibrium angle (c. 5°) of wet boulder clay and the fact that the waves sometimes build storm beaches of fine shingle on the beach. Behind these ridges water may be impounded and seems to have a softening effect on the base of the cliff.

This is but the modern continuation of a long process. In 1895 the British Association for the Advancement of Science appointed a committee to inquire into the rate of coast erosion, which some years later produced the following figures for Holderness. The period covered was 1852–1897, or 37 years, and the figures refer to sheets of the six-inch Ordnance Survey.

Sheet 197 (Hornsea)	*Average loss*	182 *feet*
„ 213 (Aldeburgh)	„ „	237 „
„ 228 (Hilston)	„ „	139 „
„ 243 (Withernsea)	„ „	245 „
„ 257 (Holmpton)	„ „	273 „

Average for all sheets .. 215 feet.
Average annual loss .. 5 feet 10 inches, nearly.

Sheppard examined earlier records of the district and has shown that erosion has gone on continuously since at least Roman times. Records of the loss of land in four townships between 1086 and 1800 have been analysed. " The coast of Holderness, from Barmston to Kilnsea, is 34½ miles long. Assuming the land has been carried away equally throughout this distance, there has been a strip of land 1089 yards wide washed away, at the average rate of 7 feet 1 inch per annum (i.e. A.D. 1086 to A.D. 1800). If the denudation since Roman times has been at the same rate, 53,318 acres, or about 83 square miles, have been lost. This is equal to a strip of land 2½ miles in width for the

whole of the distance."[1] In 1885 Reid estimated the average annual
loss at 2¼ yards. The rate, however, varies from time to time and also
in place. Groynes put out to protect Withernsea, for example, have
led to increased loss south of that town.

Erosion is severe along several parts of the coasts of Norfolk and
Suffolk, and even in what are regarded as fairly hard cliffs it is often
rapid. At Hunstanton a pill-box built on the cliff top during the
1939-45 war was partly undercut in 1948.[2] The sea eats into the
comparatively soft Lower Greensand and so causes falls of the chalk
above. It is estimated that the average rate of erosion between
Hunstanton and Heacham is of the order of a foot a year. This is
interesting, since the mouth of the Wash might be regarded as a sheltered
area.[3] Between Sheringham and Yarmouth erosion is locally serious,
and those familiar with the coast road near Bacton and the neighbouring villages will know that it has had to be relaid farther inland.
At Overstrand the sea has cut well into the cliff and has nearly undermined a large hotel and some neighbouring houses (all now pulled
down).

It is impossible and also unnecessary to comment on all places
where erosion is serious, but a few examples may be given. The
figures below for the neighbourhood of Lowestoft[4] are revealing:

Corton (North end)	1883–1905	30 *feet loss*
	1905–1927	80 „ „
	1927–1947	20 „ „
Ness Point (Lowestoft)	1883–1905	390 „ „
	1905–1927	*Resulting from defence works a gain of 40 feet is recorded, plus some 100 feet of beach built up in front of the defences.*
	1927–1947	*Loss of all beach in front of sea wall, and undermining and collapse of part of it. New defence works now nearing completion.*

[1] " The Lost Towns of the Yorkshire Coast," 1912, p. 42.

[2] It was later removed.

[3] Letter 10.9.1948 from the County Planning Officer (Norfolk) to the Regional
Controller, Ministry Town and Country Planning, Cambridge.

[4] The figures are kindly given to me by the Cambridge office of the Ministry of
Town and Country Planning.

Pakefield (on a line east from the church)	1883–1905	100 *feet loss*
	1905–1927	270 „ „
	1927–1947	250 „ „

Recently this part seems to have become more stable.

Lowestoft is in an exposed position, and is the most easterly point of this country. As explained on page 217, the coastal drift is from the north, and much is held at Yarmouth. Of recent years also changes in the form of the sand banks off shore and of the set of the currents are held to be contributory causes of the severe erosion at Lowestoft.

The Isle of Sheppey affords another instance of loss. Between Scrapsgate and the jetty, south-east of Warden Point, along a total length of five and a half miles, the loss of land between 1865 and 1906 was 103 acres, or taking an average for the whole length of the line, an annual loss of 3·8 feet. At Warden Point itself the loss reached 9·7 feet a year on an average. The subsequent evolution of the part near Warden Point is shown in Figure 5.[1]

Erosion takes place in harder rocks and cliffs, but as a rule very slowly. Records are scarce, and usually only occasional big slips, if the structure is favourable, or some spectacular change, are remembered. Chalk is a rock of intermediate hardness. Near Birling Gap, west of Beachy Head, no record is kept, but there is an estimated loss of two feet a year. This, however, is very erratic and irregular in its incidence. At Seaford there is said to be some erosion of the Chalk cliffs, but what changes occur appear to be mainly the result of frost action.

All round the coasts of Great Britain other examples could be found, and doubtless the reader will know some of them. Generalisations should be avoided, or at least used with discretion. The amount of erosion even in soft cliffs is often exaggerated, and the figures given show how it can vary with time. Local exposures of boulder clay such as those south of Aberystwyth, or those west of Criccieth, retreat comparatively quickly. These are mentioned because Cardigan Bay may all too readily be dismissed as a coast wholly formed of hard rocks. The damage in 1938 at Aberystwyth itself is worth bearing in mind.

Erosion is not a serious problem in Scotland. There are some

[1] Partly from a plan prepared by F. W. S. Stanton about 1908, and further details from information supplied to the Ministry of Town and Country Planning (Tunbridge Wells), and passed to me by Mr. H. R. Wardill.

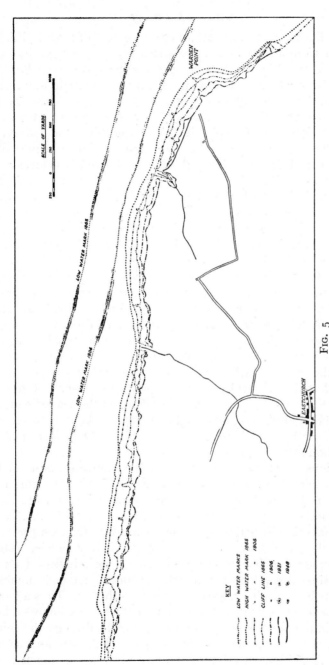

Fig. 5

Erosion in the Isle of Sheppey

(After F. W. S. Stanton and Ministry of Town and Country Planning)

places which are affected, but seldom to the extent of those in England. The Royal Commission in 1911 reported on several cases including, for instance, the Wigtownshire coast of Luce Bay between Sandhead and Drummore where local erosion has cut into the main road. Along the coast of Ayrshire and also in Arran the raised beaches (see page 257) which closely follow the coast and carry the main road are subject to some erosion. At Golspie, in Sutherlandshire, the erosion was estimated at two yards a year, a very high rate for any part of the Scottish coasts. It is still active at this place. There is also local erosion at several places along the coasts of Moray and Banff, including the Bay of Gamrie in which the picturesquely placed villages of Crovie and Gardenstown are situated. There are several other places along the east coast where erosion occurs, but in nearly all the Scottish examples the reason given to the Royal Commission was the same, namely, the local removal of shingle. It is instructive to quote from their Report: " This erosion (on the East Sands) has been going on for a long time, and within the last ten years the coastline appears to have receded about 20 or 30 feet. The erosion principally affects the property belonging to the University of St. Andrews, and it appears to have been accelerated by the removal of materials under the authority of the Corporation—who claim the foreshore—from the beach. The representative of the Corporation who gave evidence admitted that the removal greatly assisted the erosion." Removal of beach material may be important. The force of the sea expends itself on the beach, and if sand and shingle are indiscriminately taken away, especially from places where natural replenishment is slow or absent, erosion is bound to occur.

Conditions at Stonehaven afford an interesting example of local erosion. In recent years the town beaches have suffered a continuous loss of material. The littoral drift carries away material to the south, but the supplies from the north have not kept pace. Every now and again considerable quantities of material are deposited on the Stonehaven beaches, and across the mouth of the River Cowie. This in turn may cause the river to change its course near high-water mark, and also, since its velocity is thereby reduced, makes it unable to carry as much suspended material as usual to the sea. Thus a gradual rise in the level of its bed can take place. If then there follows a heavy flood, the impounded water of the Cowie breaks through the shingle, and this occasionally leads to severe scouring of the bed and banks of the river. A sudden lowering of the river bed by as much as four

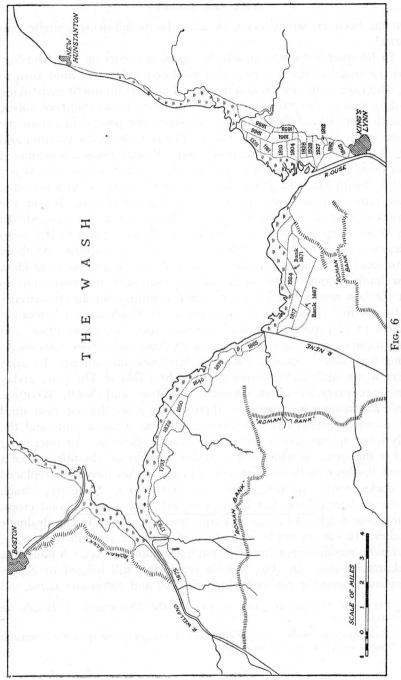

FIG. 6

Reclamations in the Wash. (After O. Borer)

feet has been known to occur in a few hours following a single rain storm.[1]

In Chapter 6 the way in which accretion occurs on Salt Marshes, and the speed of the process, are considered. Here we must turn to the wider question of accretion in general and the inning or embanking of slob lands. Accretion is most likely to occur in sheltered inlets, estuaries, or behind shingle bars. To study the process in action the coasts of the Wash should be visited. Figure 6 shows the position and extent of many recent reclamations. Since Roman times it is estimated that 8000 acres have been gained on the Norfolk side of the Wash, and in South Holland 37,000 acres. In early days banks were often built rather prematurely, but now it is realised that the longer the period of natural accretion goes on, the better the land reclaimed. In the Wash warp begins to be deposited at about +5 feet O.D.; neap tides rise to +8 feet, and at this level *Salicornia* spp. appears. At about +10 feet it is replaced by grasses. Nowadays, the foreshore outside a new bank becomes grass marsh in approximately ten years, but to get the best results it is left in a natural condition for another twenty or twenty-five years. The salt marshes in the Wash carry a vegetation typical of east coast estuaries—*Salicornia* spp., *Suaeda maritima*, and *Aster tripolium* give place to *Puccinellia maritima* and *Obione portulacoides* along the creeks. *Spartina townsendii* has been introduced. In 1925 there was a little at Wolferton and on the banks of The Cut; today there are extensive areas between Wolferton and North Wootton. Since *Puccinellia* is much grazed, there is no further development until the marsh is embanked. *Limonium* and *Armeria* are absent, and the only other species worth noting is *Cochlearia officinalis*. An interesting fact is the speed at which the ordinary halophytes[2] disappear once a marsh has been reclaimed; even within a year they have been replaced by docks, nettles, thistles, buttercups, and daisies. Since 1932 much of the reclaimed land has been ploughed, and it yields good crops. The saline origin of the ground still, however, shows in the drainage ditches; in one example in a ditch of a marsh reclaimed in 1904, *Puccinellia maritima* remained the dominant plant in 1945. A pond in a reclamation made in 1865 was 80 years later still fringed by *Scirpus maritimus*, *Puccinellia maritima*, *Aster tripolium* and *Spergularia salina*. If

---

[1] Based on information given to me by the Department of Health for Scotland.

[2] Halophytes are plants which will live in soils containing an appreciable amount of common salt or of other organic salts.

water drains from the upland, fresh water aquatics only come in very slowly.[1]

Here and elsewhere accretion on the natural marshes is encouraged by cutting ditches, or grips, running up and down the marsh. A fall of about two feet a mile is given to them, and the excavated material is usually dumped on the seaward side. This helps to produce calm water and foster deposition. If any erosion of the excavated material takes place it is spread over the grassland. The ditches are found to help the ebbing tide and to aid the consolidation of the deposited material before the next tide covers it. They are about 60 or 70 feet apart, and cut when the marshes reach about +10 feet O.D.

Apart from local variations in the nature of the marshes, exposure, and other factors, the process of reclamation in the Wash is virtually the same as that in other parts of the country. If a rapid survey is made of our coast, it will be noticed that great changes have taken place in Romney Marsh and around the Parrett mouth in Somerset, and in the reclamation of the extensive Fenlands of East Anglia and Yorkshire. More modern changes are rapidly taking place in Southampton Water and Poole Harbour and other places on the south coast. This is mainly the result of the introduction of *Spartina townsendii*, a plant which first appeared in 1870, and since then has spread very rapidly, and has been planted on many other parts of the coast to help reclamation. " The stout stem bears stiff erect leaves: from the bases of the stems stolens radiate in all directions, binding the soft mud; and feeding roots, mostly horizontal in direction, ramify through the surface layers of the mud, while stouter anchoring roots extend vertically downwards. The leaves offer broad surfaces to the silt-bearing tidal water, and their points catch and hold fragments of seaweed and other flotsam. The thick forest of stems and leaves breaks up the tidal eddies, thus preventing the removal of mud which has once settled on the marsh. . . . No other species of salt-marsh plant, in north-western Europe at least, has anything like so rapid and so great an influence in gaining land from the sea.[2]

Another district in which there has been a good deal of reclamation is Morecambe Bay. Although local conditions favour the process, the results are not of any great value, since it is sand rather than silt which is deposited. The sand is derived mainly from Triassic rocks and

[1] C. P. Petch, Reclaimed Lands of West Norfolk, *Trans. Norf. Norw. Nat. Soc.* 16, 1945, 106.

[2] A. G. Tansley, The British Islands and their Vegetation, 1939, p. 828.

boulder clay, and is chiefly quartzose and well rounded. Since, however, it is free from silt it is more or less useless. This fact was strongly emphasised by the Royal Commission (1911), and in their report they also noted that of one thousand acres reclaimed near Morecambe, nearly half had been abandoned.

In the Solway and other firths of Scotland, considerable reclamations have been carried out. There is no need to detail instances, since it is clear that as far as natural and sheltered conditions are concerned, localities in the firths are obviously suitable for this purpose, partly as a result of seaborne silt, partly of river borne material. Around Dingwall, for example, the Conon and Peffery rivers deposit a great deal of sediment. On the other hand, diversity of interests must be considered. It may seem an obvious advantage to take in more land, but on the Clyde some reclaimed lands had to be removed, since they were detrimental to the more important navigation interests.[1]

A word is desirable about the lateral spread of natural marsh. If comparisons are made between two separate editions of the six-inch Ordnance Survey of selected areas, the spread can be measured. Since the surveyors were probably not ecologists it is not always clear what boundary they took for the vegetation. In certain cases known to the writer, however, reasonable measurements can be made in this way. Nowadays the quickest method is to compare two air photographs of the same place taken a few years apart. Anchor marsh, a small enclosed marsh on Scolt Head Island, was almost bare of plants in 1920, but in 1939 it was thickly carpeted and a good deal of mud had also accumulated. Holme marsh, near the entrance to the Wash, seems to have developed from a sand flat enclosed in part by a shingle ridge to its present fairly advanced state since 1858.

Loss and gain of land are going on constantly. Erosion is nearly always more spectacular, especially if houses or other buildings are caused to fall. Yet it is the slow unnoticed process of accretion in estuaries and other places that is the more valuable. The Royal Commission in 1911 found that in total area, accretion far exceeded loss. No other comprehensive measurements have been made since then, but we can assume without any doubt that the statement is still true.

If, however, we go back in time, even only for a century, we are soon in difficulties. Much of our present fairly detailed knowledge

[1] Royal Commission on Coast Erosion and Afforestation: Final Rept. p. 135, para. 49.

depends mainly on present-day observations and measurements—all
too few—specifically designed to tell us of loss and gain. The large
scale Ordnance Survey maps are nearly always our first reliable
means of measurement, and they date back only to the early decades
of the nineteenth century. Earlier maps are seldom reliable; sometimes particular surveys are very helpful, but it is rare to find anything before the eighteenth century on which accurate distances
can be obtained. This does not mean that early maps are useless;
far from it. They must, however, be used with great caution and
their information, where possible, checked in other ways. Erosion
and accretion are both irregular in their rates of action, and for this
reason alone averages over a long period must not be taken as holding
good for other periods of similar length. All kinds of factors may
intervene; a sand bank may be thrown up offshore or in front of a
cliff and so hinder direct erosion; wearing down of the shore platform
may allow bigger waves to break near the cliff foot and so increase
the rate of loss; · if the sea is cutting into land sloping upwards to the
interior the rate will gradually decrease, since the waves have to remove
an increasing amount of waste per unit of advance; the exact con-
verse of this may lead to quicker erosion. These and many other local
factors must be taken into very careful consideration if we delve back
into the past and try to estimate loss or gain in early times.

The growth of certain shingle spits and forelands can be traced
with some approach to accuracy over long periods. Orford Ness
illustrates the point well. In 1601 it was carefully mapped by Norden,
who made a survey of the whole Manor of Sudbourne. The maps
are on a large scale and the spit itself seems to have been as carefully
surveyed as the farm land. Figure 7c shows the position of the south
end of the spit in 1601. We know that, apart from minor setbacks, the
spit lengthened until it reached a maximum in 1897, in which year
a great storm did much damage along the east coast, and cut off about
a mile of its distal end. Since then its history can be traced from
various editions of the Ordnance Survey. Before 1601 the evidence
is far less reliable. There is in the British Museum an Elizabethan
map which is undated, but probably was made about 1590. It shows
a considerable amount of detail, and the southern tip of the shingle
bar is marked opposite a point nearly half-way between Boyton Hall
and Cauldwell Hall. A map by Appleton (1588) is similar, and in
fact may have been copied from the other map, or vice versa. Both
show the Alde above Aldeburgh wrongly orientated. Saxton's (1575)

and Speed's (1610) maps are sketchy as far as the coast is concerned, and do not help us at all. Maps of the seventeenth and eighteenth centuries show the gradual southward progression of the spit, and in a broad sense are consistent with the later maps and the first Ordnance Survey map of the district, dated 1805. From that time we have fairly reliable data.

The earliest map of this part of the coast is part of a chart extending

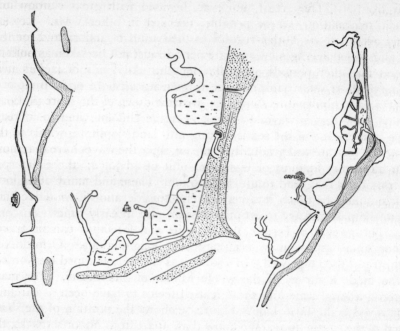

FIG. 7

Orford Ness. (a) Part of Coastal Chart said to be *temp*. Henry VIII; (b) Map, *temp*. Elizabeth; (c) Norden's Map, 1601. The position of Orford Castle is shown on the two earlier maps. See also Fig. 36

from Gorleston to the Orwell, and may have been prepared in connection with coast defence schemes. It is an attractive but rather imaginative piece of cartography, and marks the entrance to Orford Haven close to what we now call Stonyditch Point. It is not a map from which we can make measurements. It carries no date, but there is some reason for supposing that it appeared about 1530. Granting that, and assuming that the end of the spit was then more or less in the place suggested by the map, we can only conclude that the spit grew with great rapidity between 1530 and 1601 (Norden). But by Henry VIII's time the prosperity of Orford had declined: its rise had corresponded with the building of the Castle in 1165 when " shingle had begun to collect at and upon the headland, Orford Ness. The town quickly developed from the small hamlet of Sudbourne to a thriving port, and finally to a flourishing borough *standing at the very mouth of the haven.*"[1] This last statement is significant. When the shingle of the Ness had reached the neighbourhead of Stonyditch Point it would form a protection to the port of Orford. Moreover, an inspection of Stonyditch Point today shows that a number of shingle ridges end there, implying that for a considerable time the mouth of the river was approximately in that position. If this argument is sound, the Henry VIII map, which in any case is a kind of picture of the coast rather than a map in the ordinary sense, represents the coast much as it was in Henry II's time—at the period when the Castle was built and Orford was at its zenith. The gradual decay of the town is intimately linked with the menace of the ever-growing spit, but other factors have, of course, also played a part (Fig. 36, p. 153).

Orford is a spectacular example, but similar histories apply to other east coast havens, including Southwold and Yarmouth. The smaller havens of past times at Benacre and Thorpe have been completely blocked by shingle. On the Norfolk coast the westward growth of Blakeney Point was one of the main factors that led to the decay of the combined port of Blakeney-Cley-Wiveton. In a Muster Roll of 1570 these three ports exceed King's Lynn both in number of ships and mariners, and in 1582 a record shows that they jointly possessed seven ships of more than 100 tons, whereas Lynn had two and Yarmouth four. In these and all similar cases, the growth in the size of ships was a main factor in the decay of shallow water ports. Moreover, the final blow to the small ports of North Norfolk occurred when the railways were built. Even at Thornham, now truly derelict, corn was exported and coal imported almost within the memory of some still living.

Many ports and harbours on other coasts tell a similar tale, but seldom have we reliable evidence of coastal changes and evolution. Edward I built his castle at Harlech in 1286. Since it has a water-gate, it presumably at one time had easy access to the sea. There is

[1] V. B. Redstone, Memorials of Old Suffolk, Ch. XII. (The italics are mine, J.A.S.).

no known document which illustrates the condition and nature of the
coastline when the Castle was built. There are, however, several
references in the Public Record Office that make it clear that Harlech
was a port, and that the actual harbour was probably at, or very close
to, the Castle (Fig. 28). Today the Castle on its rock is well back
from the sea. The whole area of Morfa Harlech has been photographed
from the air, and a careful inspection of the mosaic and a study of the
shore processes and features of this part of Cardigan Bay indicate
that what is now Morfa Harlech began its growth as a small shingle
and sand spit south of Harlech. Growth to the north continued, and
in 1808 the marsh within the spit was embanked. From what can
still be seen, and also from inference, creeks of some size intersected
the marsh, and the havens and creeks so often referred to in the docu-
ments dealing with Harlech, may well have been those in the marsh
which developed *pari passu* with the growing spit, which in 1286 had
grown only a little so that ships could easily sail round it and come
into the harbour it enclosed. After the conquest of the Welsh, and as
a result of the constant growth of the spit, Harlech as a port declined
in importance. It is more than likely that for some time small ships
could still sail round the northern end of the spit into calm creeks
within, but a time came when this was difficult, and the final embanking rendered it impossible.[1]

Another form of rapid change in coastal areas occurs where dunes
are advancing. The full history of this subject is difficult and complicated, since in some cases, at any rate, it may be interconnected
with slight vertical changes in the relative levels of land and sea. In
South Wales there are extensive expanses of dunes, and Higgins[2] has
made a careful investigation of their growth. There are many instances
of encroachment of dunes over settlements and farm lands. The Via
Julia, dating from the first century A.D., may have passed through
what is now the north-eastern corner of Kenfig Burrows. The local
settlement was probably in use by the end of the ninth century. There
was certainly a castle in 1152, and the port was in use in 1184. The
church dates back to before 1154. The new, i.e. Mawdlam church,
was built on higher ground in 1261, and Kenfig Pool existed in 1365.

---

[1] An account of the historical fluctuations of the bar of the river Findhorn, on
the Moray Firth, is given on page 143. All river harbours deflected by a sand or
shingle bar have similar stories, but the examples given are sufficient to illustrate
the general subject.

[2] *Arch. Cambrensis*, June, 1933.

The old church was used until 1397, and the Via Julia was open until 1344, and the Castle occupied until 1403. Later, the site was obliterated by sand. " The evidence . . . makes it clear that in this region there was no apparent danger from moving sand at the close of the twelfth century, but that within a hundred years the sand in the immediate vicinity of the town itself was a danger, and that by 1485 moving sand was affecting the area beyond the town. . . ."[1] This was typical of other dunes in South Wales, and Higgins finds the evidence throughout reasonably consistent. No danger from moving sand seems to have been noticed up to the early part of the thirteenth century. There was a fairly sudden change in the fourteenth, and the records all seem to suggest that these storms blew up much sand, which greatly damaged property and agricultural land. We know that not only here but elsewhere the thirteenth and fourteenth centuries were times of great storminess, and that changes in coastal areas were then often considerable, especially in the Low Countries. It still remains to be proved whether this period was one in which a slight change of level, strongly suspected in Romney Marsh, also took place.

In Cornwall, too, there is plenty of evidence about the movement of sand and the burying of churches and other buildings. We may illustrate the matter with reference to Perranzabuloe. Dexter[2] has sifted fact from fiction and we cannot do better than follow him. The legend of the Three Churches is this: Long ago a great sandstorm overwhelmed the parish of Perranzabuloe (=Sanctus Piranus in Sabulo). The oratory or shrine of St. Piran was buried and lost for centuries. It was accidentally unearthed about a century ago. With the burying of the shrine (i.e. the *first* church), the parishioners built a second, which also suffered a similar fate, but since the threat was anticipated the parishioners took down this second Church stone by stone and re-erected it as the *third* church at Lamborne. Only the foundations of this second church were left in the sandhills, and a cross was set up to mark its site.

So much for legend; excavation and analysis have produced the facts. The Oratory was built at the head of a little fertile combe in the sixth or seventh century. It is not quite certain if St. Piran actually built it. It was an Oratory and not a parish church. Gradually

[1] L. S. Higgins, *op. cit.*

[2] A Cornish Legend: the Three Churches of Perranzabuloe. Truro, City Printing Works, 1923. Dr. N. J. G. Pounds put me in touch with various sources dealing with coastal sand areas in Cornwall.

accumulating sand caused the adjacent spring to change its course so as to threaten the western wall of the Oratory; consequently, a stone dam was built, probably during the eleventh century. The relics of St. Piran were enshrined here, and the Oratory became a mediaeval pilgrims' shrine. For this reason another doorway was made, and a new one substituted for the original Celtic doorway. This alteration was probably finished in the twelfth century. Up to the time of the Reformation the Oratory was kept clear of sand so that the relics of the saint could be seen. But when the destruction of shrines and images took place, the Oratory roof was removed. This was early in the reign of Queen Elizabeth. The Oratory was thus neglected and was gradually surrounded by sand. Yet Camden, in 1586, speaks of it as " on the sands," and Wilson[1] says it could still be seen in 1608. Soon after this the sands covered it, and it was lost, until in 1789 the shifting sands again exposed the western gable. In 1835 it was excavated by William Michell, and by William Haslam in 1843. Then it was neglected until 1892, and finally excavated and partly restored in 1910.

The Old Parish Church was built between the ninth and eleventh centuries, about one-third of a mile east of the Oratory, in order to avoid the encroaching sand. Part of this building still survives, and it is to it that the Domesday survey refers. Additions were made to this Church in the twelfth and fourteenth centuries. Up to the beginning of the seventeenth century, it was free from sand, but then mining operations diverted the stream which flowed between it and the Oratory—this stream had been a means of checking the sand advance —so that the original stream bed dried up and sand began to threaten the church. For the next two centuries various attempts were made from time to time to restrain the sand, but eventually it prevailed. *Parts* of this church were removed, but most of it was left, and it was still visible in 1848. The present church was consecrated in 1805.

Other coastal areas of north Cornwall were also ruined by sand. The Gwithian sands cover about the same area as do those at Perranzabuloe, and seem to have formed in the Middle Ages. In the seventeenth century they were a menace, and Lelant Church was invaded. East of the Hayle river these sands caused the deterioration of a considerable area of good agricultural land. Somewhat similar, but less extensive damage was done by sand advancing on to farm land south of Trevose Head. St. Constantine's Chapel was also destroyed. North

[1] The English Martyrologe, 1608, p. 116.

of the Camel estuary is an extensive dune area at St. Minver. These dunes were threatening St. Enodoc's Church in the first decade of the nineteenth century, and finally ruined it.

In all these cases there is an obvious parallel with South Wales. The present dune areas were, as far as the very slender evidence goes, quite free from sand in the sixth and seventh centuries. By the

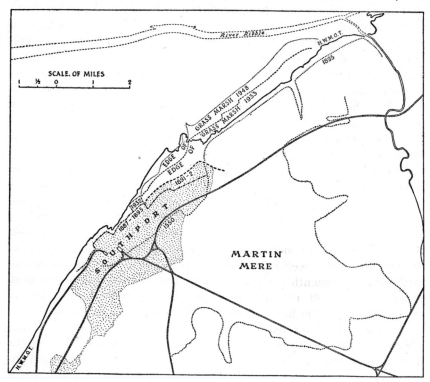

FIG. 8
Coastal Changes at Southport. (From information supplied by the Borough Surveyor)

thirteenth and fourteenth centuries dunes became a serious menace. There was apparently a more stable period in the sixteenth century, and a renewed advance later.

Southport illustrates admirably the growth of a modern town on recent accumulations of blown sand. A map dated 1736 shows the site of Lord Street, the chief thoroughfare of the town, as " The New Marsh," and washed by high tides. By 1834 a new range of dunes had formed to seaward, and " Lord Street " was then a line of slacks or fresh-water pools. Extensive reclamations were later carried out, including the extension to the North promenade, and the building of the Marine Lake and Marine Drive in 1887-1895. The last sea-bank around the Municipal Golf Links was made in 1931-32. In the Crossens district (the north-west end of Southport) considerable changes have taken place, and are shown in Figure 8. In recent times reclamation in this part has been carried out by the planting of a stretch of fore-shore below high-water mark with grass sods, or samphire, set out at about one yard intervals. These gradually grow together to form a close turf, and the level also rises with the deposition of tidal silt. When conditions are judged fit, an embankment is built to exclude the sea, and the reclaimed area is drained. In the southern part of the town and nearer Birkdale the coast has altered far less. There has been some outward growth since the coast at one time followed what is now Rotten Row.

What has been said so far shows that even during the last two or three centuries it is far from easy to make any exact assessment of coastal changes. They are known quite well qualitatively, but not quantitatively. It is only occasionally that we find reliable data which allow us to fix details with certainty. In still earlier times the record is worse, and before the period of maps and plans we have to rely on descriptions and perhaps tradition. Sometimes we can check this evidence by careful archaeological or geological excavations, but even so we seldom if ever get precise measurements except at the place of excavation, and even there the evidence is sometimes equivocal.

In Wales, Cornwall, Ireland, and Brittany there are many legends which have as their theme the overflowing of wells or lakes or the drowning of low-lying areas by the sea. In the Isles of Scilly and the neighbouring parts of Cornwall there is the legend of Lyonesse—the fertile land that formerly was supposed to extend beyond Cornwall. This land was alleged to have been overwhelmed by the sea, leaving but one survivor, a man named Trevilian, who was able to mount a swift horse and escape to the mainland. Geological and perhaps archaeological evidence certainly supports the view that land has been comparatively recently submerged in the Isles of Scilly, and although this submergence may have included the rocks called the Seven Stones, mid-way between the islands and Cornwall, there is no ground whatever for the tradition that these rocks mark the site of a large city.

Off Penmaenmawr in North Wales there is visible at low water a patch of seaweed-covered stones called Llys Helig. These have been described as the ruins of a palace which was inundated between the fourth and ninth centuries. It has been conclusively shown[1] that this story is only about a hundred years old, but it is nevertheless often regarded as history based on the authority of " An Ancient Survey of Pen Maen Mawr " by Sir John Gwynn, who, in turn, refers to earlier " authorities." According to the *Survey*, Helig and his people, when the supposed sudden inundation took place, fled to Trwyn 'r Wylfa, a hill in the parish of Dwygyfylchi, which is still sometimes referred to as the Hill of Mourning. But recent examination of the legend and also of the site of Llys Helig, has shown that the legend is a fairly modern tale, and that the palace is nothing else than a heap of large stones—the remains of a former glacial deposit, similar to the scars so frequently found on the Cumberland coast.

The most interesting example illustrating the inter-relation of physiography, geology, archaeology, and folk lore is to be found in the legend of Cantref y Gwaelod. In Cardigan Bay there are several Sarns, or causeways, running seawards from the coast. The longest is Sarn Badrig, or St. Patrick's Causeway, which runs south-west from Mochras Island for about twenty miles, nine of which may be exposed at a very low ebb. The others are shorter: Sarn y Bwch is about a mile long, Sarn Cynfelin seven or eight miles, Sarn Dewi about a quarter of a mile, and Sarn Cadwgan one and a quarter miles long. They are all formed of loose rounded stones and boulders and are quite narrow. Tradition has it that some of them represent the remains of masonry. This, however, is false; they are entirely natural features.

The first mention of the lost land, or lost hundred, of Cantref y Gwaelod occurs in the so-called Black Book of Carmarthen, which belongs to the twelfth century. There the cause of the flooding is ascribed to one Margaret or Meredig " who, at times of feasting, allowed the water of a magic well, under her charge, to overflow the country." The more popular tradition blames a certain Seithennin, who, in his cups, neglected the sluices. In course of time the legends varied, but Seithennin remains the central figure. In 1662 this story was connected with Sarn Badrig by Robert Hengwrt. Later writers embellished this suggestion, and in the eighteenth and nineteenth

[1] F. J. North, Supplement to the *Llandudno, Colwyn Bay and District Field Club Proceedings*, Llandudno, 1940.

centuries there was a collection of tales and legends to the effect that Cantref y Gwaelod had been drowned in historic times as a result of carelessness. Hence, it is not surprising to find that an actual date is ascribed to the event, namely A.D. 520. There is no historic support for this. The Romans did not occupy any of the coastal area between 55 B.C. and A.D. 409, and no mention is made either of the lost land or of the catastrophe in Antonine's *Itinerary*, or by Ptolemy, or by Giraldus Cambrensis.

Is there, then, any foundation for the inundation legend? Certain facts are important. The sarns are natural features; at Borth and other places there are submerged forests indicating changes of level; this and the existing distribution of boulder clay on and near the coast clearly imply that much of Cardigan Bay was a low lying boulder clay plain before a geologically recent subsidence or submergence took place.

Somehow or other it seems that a tale of a former land in Cardigan Bay has come down to us from remote antiquity, and it is one of many similar tales. " The numerous interesting features which these tales have in common seem to suggest the existence in past times of people who were supposed to live in lakes, were small of stature, disliked iron, possessed few articles of furniture, had not learnt the art of making bread, disliked the greensward being broken up by the plough, were successful in tending animals, had a limited ability to count, and probably used a language of their own which no-one else understood. They appear also to have reckoned descent in the female line. If this suggestion is accepted, these characteristics are consistent with a pastoral people in a primitive state of culture, who were not acquainted with the use of iron, but who attributed great importance to stocks of cattle, sheep and goats, and knew little or nothing about tilling the ground and the growing of corn."[1]

This description might well apply to the Bronze Age people, whose pile-dwellings make clear their intimate association with lakes. The later Iron Age peoples, with better weapons, must have frightened the earlier inhabitants. An anthropological investigation of Central Wales has revealed that a short, dark, and rather long-headed people are associated with remote hill lands, in fact in places where traces of Neolithic man are still common. In the Mawddach valley, around Towyn and in other places is another type. In these places Bronze Age pottery is found. The distribution of these people suggests they

[1] O. T. Jones, The Welsh Outlook, January, 1941.

came later than the dark hill folk. Later still came the iron using people.

It is, therefore, possible that the folk tales, a better description than legends, go back at least as far as the early contacts of the Iron Age people with the peoples already living in Wales, or it may be even that the tales date from the remoter past when the Bronze Age and Neolithic peoples were first in contact.

There is little doubt (see Chapters 8 and 9) that in or before the Neolithic period the boulder clay reached some distance out into Cardigan Bay as a low-lying plain through which the rivers pursued winding, sluggish courses. The post-glacial rise of sea level included the Neolithic period, but probably ceased fairly soon after it. It is likely that the submergence was wholly or nearly complete in the Bronze Age. It has been argued with conviction that many of the present inhabitants of Wales are the direct descendants of Neolithic man, and it is at least possible that their remote ancestors actually witnessed the drowning of the coastal plain. In short, we may have in the legend of Cantref y Gwaelod the gist of a folk tale that has been handed down from a very remote period of human history.

One final word: the sarns are formed of boulders that were contained in the boulder clay; there is no reason whatever for ascribing their formation to any human element. It is, however, difficult to account for their long and narrow shape. Sarn Badrig and Sarn Cynfelin occur about mid-way between river mouths, thus suggesting the idea that they are in some way continuations of the watersheds between adjacent streams.

CHAPTER 4

THE COAST
IN PROFILE AND PLAN

BEFORE discussing particular stretches of coastline formed by rocks of various types, a general review of the nature of cliffs and of the shore profile is desirable.

Let us assume that the sea comes to rest against the land at a certain level, and that that level remains unchanged for a long period of time. What will happen depends on a variety of factors, and to make the matter clear it will be convenient to discuss certain special conditions.

If the land is formed of soft rocks and is low and flat, the waves will begin to cut a slight notch in it. The notch implies a cliff and a platform, which develop concurrently. If the initial slopes of the land are gentle, the cliffs are not likely to attain any great height, but the platform can widen considerably. But in order that it may widen, it must also slope seawards. In the early stages the cliff and platform are insignificant, and only those waves reach the cliff foot which can traverse the shallow water off shore. With the increasing width of the platform, the waves crossing it lose much of their power. At the same time the larger storm waves will break near the outer edge of the platform and gradually wear it down, thus enabling other waves to traverse it. A factor of great importance in this connection is the tidal range. At high tide the platform may be covered by several feet of water and the waves can run over it and erode the cliff. At low tide the platform may be wholly or partly exposed. This statement immediately poses a difficult question. At what level are platforms cut? There is no definite answer to this, and the difficulty is not lessened if we consider cliffs and platforms around our own coasts, because it is not always clear that they are entirely the product of present-day conditions—in fact we may be reasonably certain that they often have a long and complicated history associated with former shifts of sea level.

Some writers argue that platforms are cut mainly at and near high water. In order to think about this matter it is advisable to disregard any existing platforms and consider what might happen in an ideal case. Suppose in Figure 9 AB represents average high-water level, and CD average low-water level. (This in itself is an improper simplification, since in a tidal cycle all levels between these two selected ones, as well as some above or below them, are reached). It is clear that the waves can erode effectively at all levels between the two lines. In early stages we may probably assume somewhat irregular erosion, but since it is only at and near the time of high water that the higher levels can be attacked, it is plain that erosion near the AB level is associated with high water. But at low water all or nearly all above the CD level is exposed and cannot then be eroded by the waves. With the rise of the tide, waves, at first small, but gradually increasing with the increasing depth of water, can traverse the slope DB and it seems likely that the most

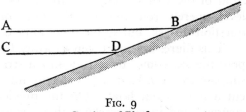

Fig. 9
Cutting of Platforms

effective erosion of this slope must take place, other things being equal, at and about high water. The bigger waves can attack it in its outer parts and gradually wear it down, and smaller but still effective waves can traverse it and attack the cliff in the rear. In ordinary conditions the waves need not be large and can travel over it easily: the differentiation in the size of the waves really only applies to the contrast between storm and normal conditions—but it is under storm conditions that the real work of erosion is so often accomplished.

It may, however, be argued that platforms are more easily cut below average low water level. It is true that below this somewhat arbitrary level the sea floor is nearly always covered with water and therefore in a position to suffer erosion. Moreover, at high water, the bigger waves can travel over it and add their quota to the erosion that takes place at (and near) low water. This may be true, but simple low water erosion presumably implies that the cliff foot should begin at that level and, except in so far as beach deposits may obscure it, at high water the cliff foot should be well submerged.

Since we are uncertain about the levels at which platforms are cut, we must either ignore, or at least refer with care, to those around our own coasts, so that we do not beg the question. However, it is likely that in soft rocks existing platforms are largely, perhaps wholly, the result of present conditions, e.g. the Carstone platform off Hunstanton and the Chalk platform around parts of Kent and Sussex. If that assumption is correct, it is almost certain that the effective cutting takes place only above mean sea level and especially near the time of high water. Low water cutting of many existing platforms at springs is impossible, and even at neaps is negligible.

Another point demands consideration by field workers. If it is assumed that an existing platform is of present-day origin and is formed mainly by waves at high water, is there any reason for thinking that waves at low water are forming a lower platform at the seaward front of the visible one? Or are waves at low water, or at mean sea level, merely rounding off the edge of this flat? These are easy questions to ask, but so far there appears to be no conclusive answer.

This digression has taken us away from our original theme. Suppose the sea comes to rest against a strip of coast of hard rocks, and suppose that the land slopes steeply into deep water. The waves will cut a notch—but how? On the previous pages a soft rock coast is assumed and in consequence there would be plenty of fine material, mud, sand, and small stones, with which the waves could attack the cliff and platform. It is true that the direct attack of the waves on a hard coast may be considerable, but it will only be so if the rocks attacked are much weathered or riddled with holes, clefts, and crannies in which the air can be suddenly compressed and released and so lead to fracture of the rocks. Waves, without sand and other ammunition, which are attacking a hard rock coast sloping steeply into deep water will have but little effect. They are reflected back from the coast, and owing to the rise and fall of the tides, to say nothing of the variability in size of the waves, the rocks are attacked through a considerable vertical range, and NOT just along a narrow strip. Thus, there is no very good reason why a notch, gradually giving way to a narrow platform and small cliff, should be formed unless conditions remain static for a long period of time.

This at once provokes the question—what is a cliff? Definitions vary, but the following is from the Shorter Oxford Dictionary: " A high steep face of rock; esp. (now) a steep face of rock on the seashore." This is a good definition, since it does not specify origin. In the preceding paragraphs, and in many writings on physical geography or geology, sea cliffs usually imply marine erosion. If this is so, we are bound to meet difficulties sooner or later. It is clear that if we associate cliff and platform together, then we must imply that the cliff is an erosion feature. The point, however, is worth making, since it is difficult, perhaps impossible, to avoid ambiguity. We speak quite properly of the cliffs of Torridon Sandstone at, e.g. Handa Island, Point of Stoer, Rhu Coigach, and Greenstone Point, so that it is difficult to avoid speaking in the same (erosive) sense of the steep slopes of the Sound of Sleat or Loch Hourn, neither of which is appreciably affected by marine erosion, present or past.

There remain, however, long stretches of the coast of Great Britain fringed by well-developed platforms and backed by fine cliffs. Perhaps the most beautiful examples are seen between Bude and Westward Ho! Many miles of platform, cut out of contorted rocks of varying hardness, are exposed at low water, but covered at high water, at which time erosion of the cliffs, at any rate in times of storm, may be severe. These platforms may be the work of waves at present sea level, but they may equally owe part or even most of their formation to conditions existing when the more recent raised beaches were formed. On the other hand, if the *Patella*[1] beach is studied in parts of south Cornwall and south Devon it will be noticed that there are often remains of a definite platform, frequently covered by Head. The *Patella* beach, however, is probably inter-glacial, and if the present rock platforms are not wholly of modern origin, they may perhaps be associated with more recent fluctuations of sea level than those applicable to the *Patella* beach.

To return, however, to the cliffs. Their form varies with many factors. First of all there is the topography of the original land, which may be flat and low-lying, rugged, rolling, or mountainous. The sea will come to rest against the land at a given level, and the " high steep faces of rock " will depend first on what the land is like. Later marine erosion may modify the original slopes, provided that wave action can be effectively directed toward them.

If waves attack a land formed of more or less horizontal rocks there is the likelihood of nearly vertical cliffs being produced. This is especially noticeable if the various strata are of unequal hardness. Good examples occur at Hunstanton, Lyme Regis, and on the coast of Glamorganshire. If the strata composing the cliff dip seawards, the

[1] See page 260.

cliff form is likely to vary greatly in detail. Sometimes it may overhang, but the general slope of the surface above the part directly
attacked by the sea may well leave a stronger impression on one's
mind than does the lower part of the cliff, which is likely to be steep.
If the strata are inclined away from the coast the cliff slope is as a rule
moderate. These simple cases can easily be visualised. In nature the
form and structure of cliffs are very variable. Chalk Cliffs (see page
82) are often nearly vertical independently of their structure. This
is presumably the outcome of the effects of marine and subaerial
erosion on a rock of great homogeneity, good jointing, and often
marked bedding. The profile of the cliffs of north Devon varies a
good deal, but is locally steep—immediately north of Hartland Quay
there is a range of high and almost vertical cliffs which are made up
of sharply folded beds. On the other hand, soft rocks often form steep
cliffs. The boulder clay cliffs of Holderness and of north Norfolk, or
again around Criccieth and Afon Wen are soft and easily eroded by
the waves. For this reason they are undercut and steepened. But local
composition and height play their parts. The glacial cliffs near
Sheringham are c. 100 feet high and steep, often tumbled, and composed not only of boulder clay, but sand and gravels. The natural
angle of slope of these materials, even if partly consolidated, will not
allow of verticality. Farther north the lower and, on the whole, more
homogeneous Holderness cliffs sometimes approach the vertical.

In parts of north Devon and Somerset the slope of the land to the
sea is decidedly steep. It is not in any sense a cliff of marine erosion,
and the effect of the action of the sea can be noted at the bottom of
the slope, which has been cut back into a low cliff. Comparisons
between various parts of the Cornish coast bring out differences of
this sort clearly. The relatively sheltered parts of the southern coast
are fringed by low cliffs, whereas on the exposed parts of the northern
coast there are fine and bold ones. But here again it is worth pausing
to consider their origin. It looks as if these cliffs are entirely of modern
formation, i.e. since the present levels of land and sea existed. But
is this so ? In order to illustrate this point turn for a moment to the
Gower Peninsula, where there are some fine limestone cliffs at the
foot of which are many traces of raised beaches. These remnants,
whilst commonest in sheltered spots, are not only found in such places.
A similar raised beach platform may have existed along north Cornwall; the remains of beaches in the Camel estuary and on the south
coast are suggestive. Thus, it may be that the existing Cornish cliffs

are far from being wholly produced under modern conditions. It is more than probable that they are but the slightly modified forms of much earlier formed cliffs, just as are those in the Gower peninsula. The same is true of the magnificent Old Red Sandstone cliffs near Duncansby Head in Caithness. The Geological Survey Memoir notes that the stacks seem to rise from a low platform, part of which may be found at the cliff foot. These are merely examples; many others could be given. They serve to show that our knowledge of cliff form and evolution is still in an elementary condition. More studies, such as that by Miss Arber[1] on the cliff profiles of Devon and Cornwall, are wanted before we can make any real advance in our knowledge of cliff scenery.

Before leaving this question, consider the western coast and islands of Scotland. In Chapter 8 it is shown that much of this area is all that remains of a former great plateau of lava. The disposition of the lavas and sills in Skye, Eigg, Mull, and other islands shows that these rocks once covered far greater areas. In Skye the cliffs are often largely or wholly formed of lavas and sills. No part of the island is fully exposed to the Atlantic, but nevertheless severe storms attack its shores. On its more exposed south-westerly facing side, there are some magnificent cliffs near Talisker Bay and Loch Brittle. Waterstein Head, farther north, is an imposing cliff of lavas and sills. At the foot of the major cliff is a low projection which is eroded by the waves; it does not follow that the major cliff above is similarly formed. In the comparatively calm waters of Loch Bracadale there are several instances of vertical cliffs to which it is impossible to ascribe an entirely marine origin. The east coast of Skye facing the island of Raasay is steep, and the cliffs are for the most part made of lava flows and sills resting on Mesozoic rocks, and fringed by a boulder beach. Raasay Sound is narrow and protected: it is difficult to suppose that cliffs along it are simply formed by wave action—in fact the green, steep slopes of the Mesozoic rocks of Skye imply that marine erosion is negligible. Judd many years ago showed that a fault probably runs along this Sound. It is known that faulting and foundering have broken up all this former volcanic area. Thus many lines of steep cliffs in lavas and sills are primarily fault-formed, and only secondarily modified by wave action. Since it is not for a moment supposed that the sides of sea lochs are the product of wave erosion, there is no reason for thinking that in places like the Sound of Sleat or the Sound

[1] *Geogr. Journ.*, 114, 1949, 191.

of Mull, marine erosion has accomplished serious cliff erosion. The steep cliffs fringing so many parts of Skye and other islands, in relatively protected waters, are probably no more than the slightly (often very slightly) wave-modified slopes produced in some other way, in western Scotland sometimes by faulting.[1]

Another feature which throws light on this problem is often seen in Scotland. As shown in Chapter 9 the present coast may be fringed for miles by raised beaches, usually by the 25-foot beach. This bench, which may be two or three hundred yards or more wide, forms almost a promenade attached to the land, and is backed by the old grass-grown cliffs. It is being eroded by the waves today; only where it is poorly developed have the waves cut through it and are now attacking the cliff behind, which is in those places clearly a composite cliff. How long this raised beach platform took to form is not known; it has not been greatly worn away in recent times and the cliffs cut in it are merely low crags and quite unlike the old cliff behind the beach, or the often numerous stacks on the beach platform. It is true that the coastline of most of England and Wales fails to show raised beach remains like those in Scotland, but the evidence in Scotland, Cumberland, Gower, Cornwall and elsewhere, makes one hesitate in ascribing many other English cliffs wholly and automatically to modern conditions.[2]

Cliff scenery varies greatly from place to place. In Chapter 5 an analysis is given of certain lines of cliffs. Here there is only need to emphasise the importance of major structural lines. If a series of gentle folds runs more or less parallel with the coast, cliffs may be eroded along them, whilst at some other locality they cut across the folds (see page 204). The form of cliffs also depends largely on the structure and nature of the land in which they are being cut. Much of the beauty of a cliffed coast depends not merely upon the details of marine erosion in various rock types, but on the occurrence of rivers debouching into the sea. In Lyme Bay there are a number of small streams which reach the sea by percolating through the shingle. The valleys have been cut down to, or even below, sea level, but the present streams are not powerful enough to keep their mouths clear. The streams at Chideock, Charmouth, and Burton Bradstock are examples.

[1] It is not implied that, even if this is the case, the present cliffs represent actual fault scarps. They may perhaps be regarded as fault-line scarps.

[2] Along much of the Durham coast the cliffs are not of modern origin in the sense of being formed wholly by the sea at its present level. Low flats occur in front of several lines of cliff, and stacks wholly or partly above present sea level are found on them.

On the other hand powerful rivers usually have wide open mouths. There are, however, other factors to consider. The Stour and Orwell in Essex, the Ouse and Arun in Sussex, the Tamar and Fal in Cornwall possess many similarities, but also exhibit important differences. It is true to say of all that the existing streams and conditions could not have produced the present features. In each case there has been a drowning of the lower part of the river, and since the river mouths may separate lines of cliff, they add enormously to the beauty of the coast. A walk along any cliffed coast may be made rather more strenuous by these breaks, but it is unquestionably more interesting.

If, however, the streams are small or if for some other reason their downward erosion has not been able to keep pace with either the change of level or with the inward erosion of the sea, the valley will have its mouth part way up the cliff face, and the stream in it will fall into the sea by one or more cascades. Coastal waterfalls are often extremely beautiful. The finest examples in England and Wales are between Boscastle and Westward Ho![1] The watershed along this coast runs close to the sea, so that all the streams are short. The nature of a fall depends mainly upon whether the stream is draining a flat-topped cliff or one of the hog's-back type. The former type, under natural conditions, may be spectacular, the latter rather uninteresting, e.g. falls at Glenthorne and Woody Bay. Litter Water has a vertical fall of 75 feet, and illustrates the rapid incutting of the sea. But some examples of this type of fall have been altered as a result of landslips; Hobby Water and Cleave Fall have, in fact, been obliterated in this way. On the other hand, the dip, strike, and hardness of the rocks play an important part. Milford Water illustrates this extremely well. It is one of the bigger streams, and there are really five individual falls. The uppermost (see top centre of Plate III, p. 66) is a dip fall, at the bottom of which there is a right-angled turn and the stream flows along a gutter following the strike. There is then another right-angled turn to form a short steep fall running contrary to the dip (the one at the bottom right of Plate III) and beyond it are two smaller falls.

In one or two cases the streams used to run in their lower courses roughly parallel with the coast. Erosion cutting into the more vulnerable parts of the cliffs more quickly than in other places has succeeded in interrupting their courses, so that a stream may now cascade into the sea rather higher up its valley than was originally the case. The

[1] E. A. N. Arber, The Coast Scenery of North Devon, London, 1911. See also W. G. V. Balchin, Trans. Roy. Geol. Soc. Cornwall, 17, 1946, 317.

lower valley is now dry. The valley of Speke's Mill has been truncated by the sea near St. Catherine's Tor.

There are numerous other examples. In the Old Red Sandstone coasts of eastern Scotland falls are not uncommon; that in the geo[1] at Crawton is a perpendicular cascade. But perhaps the finest coastal waterfalls in Scotland are in the lava areas of the Western Isles. The northern part of Skye is almost wholly formed of lava flows and sills, except that on the east coast the lavas overlie more or less horizontal Mesozoic rocks. The streams draining the interior often tumble over the abrupt cliffs in beautiful cascades. The fall of the stream draining Loch Mealt is well known, but others of like nature occur in Loch Bracadale, Talisker Bay, and elsewhere. At Invertote and Bearreraig Bay, both on the Sound of Raasay, are two handsome falls. In the first the stream has cut through the lava, and cascades over the Mesozoic rocks; in the second the lava is still largely intact. Waterfalls of this type usually imply small streams; a major river might have cut down to sea level. Moreover, their volumes fluctuate a great deal with the rainfall. Since the streams are short and drain but small areas, they are best after heavy rains.

Another feature that has a great effect on the form of cliffs are the coastal plateaus (see pages 176-178). The lower ones, and presumably the newer, are the best preserved, and often form extremely level surfaces cut across rocks of different types. The plateau at 180 feet in the Tenby peninsula is very sharply cut (Plate XXIV, p. 245).

Whatever their origin, the cliffs cut in the lower platforms necessarily show a flat and even crest line, a feature clearly visible in parts of South Wales and Cornwall. Sometimes traces of older platforms can be found inside the one now forming the cliff top, and appear as flat-topped cliffs inside and above the modern ones. It is relevant to note here that rivers cut down through these platforms and have their mouths at sea level. Thus the great powers of marine and fluviatile erosion in comparatively recent geological times can be contemplated.

It would be possible to expand this account of cliff form almost indefinitely. Each line of cliff has its own special features, and all are worthy of study. Nevertheless the reader will easily imagine variation of form and will undoubtedly know of particular cases. The boulder

---

[1] In northern Scotland geo, or sometimes goe, is a term applied to a deep and narrow inlet, usually with steep sides, and cut in hard rock. They are extremely well developed in the Old Red Sandstone of Kincardine, Caithness, and the Orkney Islands.

clay on the chalk at Flamborough Head, the soft sandy cliffs in the Crags and Westleton Beds of the Suffolk coast, the easily eroded Tertiary rocks of Bournemouth Bay, are all steep, all soft, bnt all quite different. The possibilities are endless, but each in its natural condition is beautiful and interesting.

There is another way in which cliffs can be considerably modified. If circumstances are favourable landslides may take place. There are several well-known examples, but that at Dowlands, east of Axmouth, is perhaps the most impressive. In order to appreciate the causes which produced the slipping, the following table of rock succession is relevant:

Clay with Flints.

. . . .

Chalk $\begin{cases} \text{Middle} \\ \text{Lower} \end{cases}$

Upper Greensand $\begin{cases} \text{Calcareous sandstones and Chert Beds.} \\ \text{Foxmould (Sands).} \\ \text{Cowstones (lenticular concretions of cal-} \\ \quad \text{careous sandstone in sands).} \end{cases}$

Gault (sandy clay).

. . . .

Lower (Blue) Lias (Limestones and Shales).
Rhaetic (Limestones, Shales, Marls).
Keuper Marls.

The dotted lines represent unconformities. Briefly, the cause of the slips depends on the dip, the unconformity beneath the Gault, and the relation of both to sea level. If the junction plane between the Foxmould and underlying clay occurs above sea level, and if it also slopes seawards, erosion of the cliff face removes the outward support of the beds, and so the upper layers slide forward over the lower after periods of heavy rain. This is what has happened at Hooken, and between Axmouth and Lyme Regis. At Beer Head and Whitecliff the unconformity is nearly all below water, and since the cliffs above are wholly of Cretaceous rock, falls of chalk drop directly on to the shore. Slipping of this sort produces undercliffs, the form of which depends among other things on the angle of dip, and also on the nature of the rocks which have slipped. If the rocks are coherent, large unbroken masses may slide down, as at Dowlands; in clays and softer rocks a species of mud glacier may be produced.

Near Dowlands the inland cliffs are of chalk, and the undercliffs are made of much disturbed Cretaceous material. The great chasm was formed in 1839. Since the previous June there had been much rain, and several gales. Fissures and cracks began to appear on the cliff top before Christmas, 1839, and on December 23 one of the cottages began to subside. By 5 p.m. the cottage was settling rapidly, and other cottages soon followed suit. The great slip itself occurred on Christmas night. "During December 26 the land that had been cut off by the fissures in the cliff-top gradually subsided seawards, and by the evening had reached a position of equilibrium in the undercliff. A new inland cliff, 210 feet high in its central portion and sinking to east and west, had thus been exposed, backing a chasm into which some twenty acres of land had subsided. The length of the chasm was about half a mile, while its breadth increased from 200 feet on the west to 400 feet on the east."[1] In all, some eight million tons of earth foundered. The movement also caused a ridge of Upper Greensand (Foxmould and Cowstones) to rise in the sea near the beach; it was about three-quarters of a mile long, and reached 40 feet above sea level at high water. The beds were much broken, and the mid-part of the ridge was connected to the mainland by shingle. The reef very soon disappeared, but the main chasm remains much as it was, except that most of the large pinnacles have gone. Nearly the whole of the area is now covered with vegetation, and the relative movement of the strata has produced a very uneven terrain and varied plant habitats. In Dowland's Chasm, ash has sown itself abundantly and in several places natural ashwoods, including quite large trees, have developed. They are fine examples of self-sown virgin woodland, a rare phenomenon in present-day Britain. There is no part of the British coast on which there exists such a great extent of varied wild vegetation—a rich field for future research.

There have been several other slips in this neighbourhood, all of which were similarly caused. Another example of major slipping is found at Folkestone Warren. Various ideas have from time to time been put forward to explain these slips, but the most recent views of W. H. Ward[2] are interesting. His sections show that the slips are primarily caused by the erosion of the Gault toe by the sea, and that the slips are rotational (i.e. turning about a horizontal axis) in character. The plane on which slipping takes place penetrates the full thickness of the Gault, and there is no suggestion that the Chalk is

[1] M. A. Arber, *Proc. Geol. Assoc.*, 51, 1940, 257.
[2] *Geogr. Journ.* 105, 1945, 170.

Plate I SHOREHAM HARBOUR: the harbour mouth was fixed in 1821; previously the spit extended much farther east. The beach drift is from the west (towards the observer), and this is indicated by the individual groynes as well as by the harbour piers

Plate II THE COAST SOUTH OF BUDE: flat-topped cliffs cut in alternating sandstones and shales of Upper Carboniferous Age. The photograph illustrates the varying hardness of the beds

sliding down the surfaces of the Gault. Ward is also of the opinion that the Axmouth slip was rotational.

There are many other examples of local slipping, including the Tertiary beds of the Isle of Wight facing the Solent, and the undercliff near Niton in the south of the Island. Landslips include a wide variety of phenomena from the great slip at Axmouth to the almost constant loss of sand and fine pebbles that takes place on the high cliffs at Beeston and Skelton Hills, near Sheringham. This constant loss is not a landslip in the normal sense of the word, but any slide forward or downward, whether big or little, ought to be included.

This chapter began with some reference to the development of the profile of cliffs. It would have been perhaps more logical to have followed or preceded that section by a consideration of the structure in plan. But it is difficult to deal in strict sequence with a series of topics of which the effect, or the application, of all may take place concurrently.

When the sea abuts against a land mass, no matter what the form of that land may be, it begins to attack it, and naturally the weaker rocks suffer most readily. A great deal, however, depends upon the arrangement of the strata in relation to the sea, in other words, on the structure of the land mass.

In the early stages, the waves will make the coast more irregular than it was initially, since they are cutting and trimming all the more easily removed parts. In course of time the waves smooth and round off projections and with the material thus produced cut cliffs and build beaches. It is sometimes contended that beaches of various kinds are best developed in the youthful stages of shoreline evolution, and that as time goes on the coast is more and more simplified so that the original great variety of beaches gives way to simplicity or even monotony. Text-books sometimes depict the various stages of evolution as in Figures 10a, b, c, d. This evolutionary view is broadly correct, but the diagrams are only of general application.

Perhaps the nearest equivalent in these islands to the type of coast illustrated in Figures 10a, b, c, d is that of south-western Ireland,[1] or, on a smaller scale, the coast of Pembrokeshire.[1] Both these may be regarded as in the stage of youth. Another stage intermediate between 10c and 10d is represented by the coast between Start Point and the River Dart (Fig. 11, p. 59). The rocks are relatively soft, and smooth

[1] The major features of the coastlines of south-west Ireland and Pembrokeshire are the result of drowning; local details are the result of erosion or accretion.

shingle and sand beaches occur at Bee Sands, Hallsands, Slapton, and Blackpool. The coast between Speymouth and Rosehearty on the Moray Firth is an example of one formed of hard and often metamorphic rocks, all much folded. The folds run almost at right angles to the coastline and the detail is crenulate in pattern. Along east Norfolk and Suffolk the cliffs are composed of Pliocene Crags and more recent gravelly and sandy beds which physiographically differ but little from the crag. All are soft and the sea has cut back and regularised the coast, and built beaches which may dam back the small streams or deflect the larger ones. The same type of coast occurs in Essex, but at first sight it looks very different because marine forces have so far not been able to build bars of sand or shingle across the river mouths, and the coast remains decidedly irregular. This contrast is worth bearing in mind, because useful though schematic diagrams are, they often give somewhat misleading ideas, especially if an attempt is made to fit them to an actual stretch of coast.

A distinction is usually made between submerged and emerged shorelines, and perhaps neutral shorelines may also be added as a separate class. Theoretically this is sound; but in practice it is not always so easy to apply the terms, or rather to say that a particular sequence of events is characteristic of either submergence or emergence. A land mass sinking down so that the waves come to rest against a contour line is more than likely to have an irregular shoreline, whereas a shoreline resulting from the uplift of part of a shallow sea floor will probably be fairly simple in outline, especially if deposition has had time to blot out any irregularities that may have existed.

In a general way it is true to say that throughout these islands the coastline is a submerged one. But it is not so merely as a result of one particular movement of land or sea which brought the sea against the land at the present level. Even now (Chapter 9) there is slight movement still in progress. Our shores are submerged mainly on account of the rise of sea level in post-Glacial times. There is every reason to believe that immediately after the Ice Age, sea level was about 200 feet lower than at present. But it also follows that since the Ice Age was characterised by more than one advance and retreat of the ice, the sea level before, during, and after the Glacial period must have fluctuated considerably. Hence, our coasts have been alternately uplifted and depressed relative to sea level, and it by no means follows that they are back at precisely the same height at which they stood in pre-Glacial times.

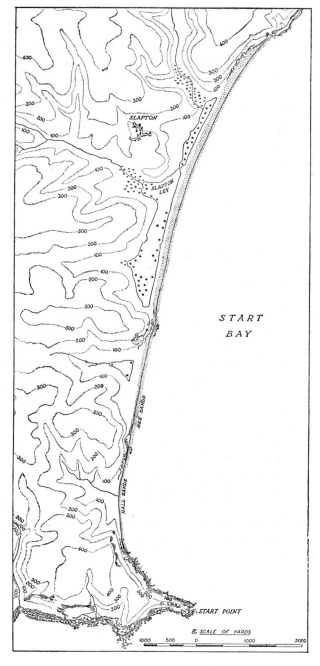

FIG. 11
The coast between
Start Point and the
River Dart. (Based
on Ordnance Survey)

START
BAY

SLAPTON

SLAPTON
LEY

BEE SANDS

HALL SANDS

START POINT

SCALE OF YARDS

The north coast of Canna is faced by a line of black and nearly perpendicular cliffs. Unfortunately their northern aspect obscures their beauty. The whole island consists of lavas and sills, and a line of fine cliffs also faces west. The other parts of the coast are lower. The bright green appearance of the interior, the lines of interior cliffs and the frequency of columnar structures, make this small island most attractive. Muck is generally similar (Fig. 12).

Eigg, too, presents some striking features. The northern part, indeed nearly the whole island, is formed of basaltic lavas. In the north they rest on Jurassic sediments which give grassy slopes and make the lower ground around Cleddale. The north-east is thus a high plateau, sloping upwards to the north, and breaking off to the west, north, and east very abruptly. The great lava flows, often markedly columnar, give a strongly terraced appearance to the island. Along the east coast steep slopes reach sea level, but there are no true

FIG. 12
Dykes on the Coast of Muck. (After A. Harker)

erosion cliffs. The Sgurr is the most spectacular feature of the island. From the north it appears as a great perpendicular monolith. By sailing round the island one can obtain a reasonable appreciation of this interesting feature. It is a long line of whitish rock running parallel with the south coast, and ending in fine abrupt precipices to the southwest. It is a great sheet of pitchstone, the origin of which is still debatable. Harker concluded it was an intrusion, whereas Sir A. Geikie, and more recently Sir E. B. Bailey, consider it as a series of subaerial lava flows filling a valley eroded in the basalts (Fig. 15, p. 66).

In western Skye are some of the finest precipitous cliffs in lava in these islands. At Talisker the flows vary from 6·or 8 feet to 40 feet in thickness. At Dunvegan Head, about 1000 feet high, there are at least 25 sheets averaging about 40 feet thick. Perhaps the best development of a basaltic coast occurs between Loch Bracadale and Loch Brittle. In this stretch the basalts descend below sea level and give rise to a

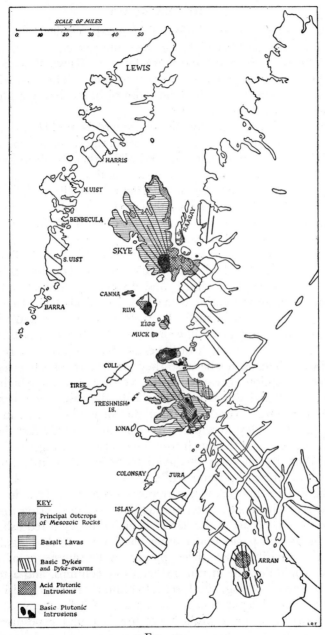

Fig. 13
Igneous Rocks in the Western Isles and Mainland of Scotland
(Based on Geological Survey)

great range of precipitous cliffs, often nearly vertical, and ranging
from 500 to even 900 feet high, the maximum being reached at Beinn
nan Caithearn. Since the cliffs are formed of lava flows and sills,
they bear a close resemblance to stratified rocks. The sills, which are
markedly cross-jointed, are here no more resistant than the lavas, and
so the whole shows one great face.

On the eastern coast of Skye the Jurassic rocks are below the basalts.
But the great sills, often exceeding 100 feet in thickness, which penetrate
these rocks, also strengthen them, and allow them to form prominent
cliffs. The higher basalts often form another, inner line of cliffs,
behind, and roughly parallel to the actual sea cliffs. The varying
thickness of the sills, their inclination and their local frequency give
much variety to the scenery. In general, the sills are harder than the
lavas, and so they stand salient.

If in any locality the inclination of the sills is but slight, flat-topped
hills may be formed. MacLeod's Tables, west of Dunvegan, illustrate
this. If a sill is steeply inclined, and divides the summits into sharp
steps where columnar jointing is marked, a vertical element enters into
the scenery, and often in such places detached masses and pinnacles
stand out from the general line of the cliffs. Sometimes this is also
true of dykes, but very often in Skye the dykes weather more rapidly
into hollows. This is not because they are formed of softer rock, but,
in Harker's opinion, because of the vertical posture which makes
attack easier; " and this is most markedly the case where a multiple
dyke has presented several vertical planes of weakness . . . in a short
space. Any tendency to a platy fracture in an undivided dyke tells
in the same sense, and the much commoner cross-jointing also facilitates
disintegration by allowing the dyke to divide into little horizontal
prisms which are easily removed."[1]

Probably the best-known example of columnar lava in western
Scotland is at Fingal's Cave on Staffa. The lava in the cave and along
much of the west coast of the island is underlain by a red ash, and at
Meallan Fulaan it passes under other basaltic flows. At Fingal's Cave
the lava is divisible into three parts ; a bottom zone of massive
columns, a middle zone of thin rather wavy columns, and a top zone
largely composed of slag. Both sets of columns are clearly visible, and
there is no line of separation in the basalt. Not far away, at Rudha
na h'Uamha in western Mull, there are beautiful exposures in the
cliffs of lava flows showing columnar structure. These lavas invaded

[1] *Mems. Geol. Survey*, The Tertiary Igneous Rocks of Skye, 1904.

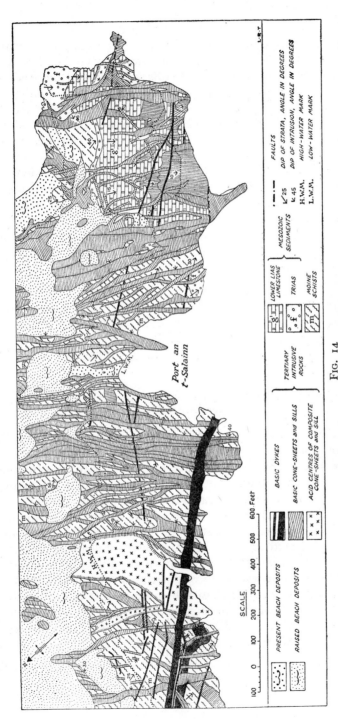

FIG. 14

Part of the South Coast of the Ardnamurchan Peninsula. (Based on Geological Survey)

a forest, for in more than one instance there are trees preserved in the lavas or breccias. " An actual tree trunk was discovered by Macculloch embedded in lava along the coastal cliffs south-west of the wilderness. . . . The trunk is represented by a cast infilled with ' white trap ' (i.e. bleached basalt) and charred wood, five feet across and forty feet in height. It stands erect, surrounded by a remarkable columnar basalt."[1] The horizontal element in the scenery of much of the island of Mull is perhaps best appreciated from a ship, but the views seawards from the high ground near Dervaig also emphasise it. The view across the Sound of Iona looking toward the north-western corner of the Ross of Mull, with Ardmeanach and Ben More also in sight, is an instructive one in the way it illustrates the effect of different types of rock on scenery. The foreground of Lewisian Gneiss, the pinkish granite east of the Sound, the glaciated granite knobs, the horizontal

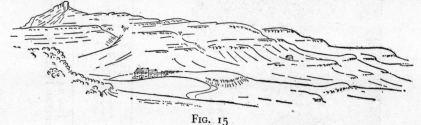

FIG. 15

Eigg—showing the Sgurr and the terraced appearance of the island.
(After A. Harker)

nature of the basalt country, and the great volcanic pile of Ben More are unforgettable.

Sills of igneous material, if on a big scale, may be sufficient to form islands by themselves. In the Shiant group, there are two main islands, Garbh Eilean and Eilean an Tighe, tied by a shingle beach (Fig. 16). The former is over 500 feet high and on its northern side is bounded by sheer cliffs. Farther to the east the lower part of the cliffs is scree-covered and partly overgrown. Eilean an Tighe, just over 400 feet high, is also bounded by high cliffs. Both islands are essentially formed of a single sill of dolerite, some 500 feet thick, and inclined at angles of 10°–15° to the south-west. Consequently the western sides of both islands have comparatively gentle slopes, whereas the scarp slopes to north and east give almost vertical cliffs, except that the great boulders fallen from them collect at their foot. The sill

[1] *Brit. Regional Geology*: Scotland, The Tertiary Volcanic Districts, 1948, p. 42.

Plate III SPEKE'S MILL MOUTH: the Mouth of Milford Water (North Devon) consists of a series of falls over steep cliffs made of highly folded rocks. The top fall is clearly a dip fall; the hidden middle part is mainly a gutter (strike) fall, and the lower fall is contrary to the dip. There is still another fall before the water reaches the sea

Plate IV STAFFA: the basalt of which the island is made is clearly visible, and the relation of the caves, including Fingal's Cave, to the columnar basalt is shown

The Scotsman

also shows columnar structure, both the diameter and length of the columns being far greater than in Staffa. The columns are nearly straight, but curve slightly near their summits on Eilean an Tighe and on parts of the north face of Garbh Eilean, where some individual columns are 350 feet high, and have an average diameter of five feet. Whilst the columns are generally hexagonal, other patterns also occur.

Apart from the columnar jointing there is also another set of major joints running approximately north-north-east and south-south-west. On the cliff face on the north of Garbh Eilean near Glaic na Crotha, they have a marked effect, and the rock is broken into great and roughly parallel slabs, instead of into individual columns. On the south-west of the same island, where the coast is very steep, there is a similar phenomenon, and there, too, the columns overhang and fall into the water. Hence, some of the big joints have opened out and great fissures running in a northerly direction into the rock have been made by wave action working along lines of weakness formed along these major joints.

The adjacent island, Eilean Mhuire, is also cliff-girt, but is made up of nearly horizontal sills of dolerite separated by three beds of Jurassic strata. To the west of Garbh Eilean is a chain of small islands, called collectively Galtachean. They too are composed of dolerite, probably the remnant of a great single sill. All show well marked columnar structure. The inclination is very variable and the curvature of the columns often conspicuous. All the Galtachean have steep and rocky north-facing cliffs. The Fladda isles are also doleritic and show good columnar structure, caves, and other similar features. They are interesting, but not as spectacular as the Shiants.[1]

The little Isle of May in the Firth of Forth is another example of a single sill, in this case inclined to the north-east at a low angle. Here again the dip slope is gentle, and there is a steep slope to the south and west. There are many east-west faults cutting through the island, which, while they have caused little if any displacement, have nevertheless broken the dolerite so that the sea has been able to eat out gullies or geos along these lines of weakness. In the northern, and flatter, part of the island, the geos allow water at high tide to pass through the island. Another interesting feature is that although columnar jointing is often conspicuous in the western cliffs, it is

[1] F. Walker, The Geology of the Shiant Islands, Quart. Journ. Geol. Soc., 86, 1930, 355.

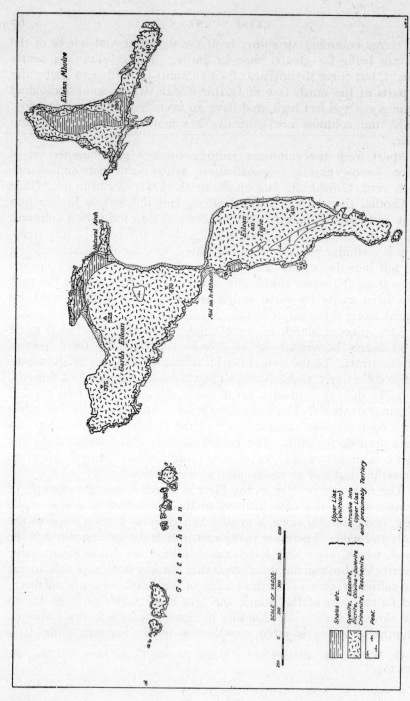

FIG. 16.—The Shiant Islands. (After F. Walker)

Eilean Mhoire

Natural Arch

Eilean an Tighe

Garbh Eilean

Maol na h-Athadh

Galtachean

SCALE OF YARDS

Shales etc. } Upper Lias (Whitbian)

Intrusive into Upper Lias and presumably Tertiary

Syenite, Essexite, Picrite, Olivine-Dolerite, Crinanite, Teschenite,

Peat.

Plate 1. WATERSTEIN HEAD. This headland (976 feet) is formed wholly of basalt flows. Note the relatively modern minor cliffing near sea-level. The Outer Hebrides can be seen.

effectively masked by jointing parallel to the cooling surface of the sill. Other major joints have also played a great part in cliff structure; they have led to the development of rock stacks and arches, the best examples being the Mill Dorr just north of Pilgrim's Haven. On the gentle north-east side the dip and jointing are approximately parallel, and a group of skerries, called the Middens, has been produced a short distance offshore.

The cliffs reach a maximum height of 150 feet on the western side, and there are clear traces of raised beaches at 50 feet, and probably at 25 feet and 100 feet. Marine erosion has therefore made great use of the lines of weakness in the sill to give it its present features. It is not, however, clear how far the features are the product of present-day conditions of sea level.

There are many other examples of sills and lava flows that might be given from the western isles of Scotland. As another instance, however, consider the Great Whin Sill which provides such striking and characteristic features on the Northumberland coast. There are various outcrops on the coast, but the main one is that between Dunstanburgh Castle and Cullernose Point. At both these headlands good columnar structure is seen in the high cliffs facing north at Dunstanburgh and south at Cullernose. Between the two places the sill has a seaward inclination, and between tide marks the water is washing a clean surface, much broken by rough and irregular jointing, although pentagonal outlines are commonest. There are also enlarged joints, crush-lines, and small faults, nearly all of which trend east or north-east. There is a major break at Craster harbour, Hole o' the Dyke, which appears to be due to a crush belt. In it is a mass of Whin showing joints running in all directions. Since the inclination is seaward, the ground rises inland, and a few hundred yards from the shore the Whin forms a fine escarpment facing westwards. Thus, most of the shore exposure corresponds to the gentle slopes we have met in the Shiant Islands and in the Isle of May.

In strong contrast to the dark cliffs of basalt and dolerite are the pink and grey cliffs of granite in the Land's End Peninsula, the Isles of Scilly, Peterhead, and a few other places. Granite varies a good deal within itself, but it is characteristic of it that it often weathers into great cuboidal masses. The form of cliffs will, however, depend a great deal upon the nature and inclination of the joints and of other lines of weakness. Often granite cliffs form fine castellated masses, since both marine and subaerial erosion work quicker along joints and other planes of weakness, thus causing the solid rock in between to stand salient as buttresses and walls. This is excellently developed between Land's End and Penberth, where the cliffs are steep and subject to the full onslaught of the Atlantic. There are many coves, and the cliff top, over which salt spray is blown, is a fine open heather-covered moorland reaching as far as St. Levan. Nearer Lamorna, the cliffs have a gentler slope and are less spectacular; much the same is true near Land's End.

The bizarre features of granite weathering, partly marine, partly subaerial, are remarkably displayed in the Isles of Scilly, which are wholly granite islands, probably at one time part of a larger mass like Bodmin Moor, or any of the other granite masses of Cornwall and Devon. They are now partly drowned, and subjected to powerful marine erosion. The sea has eaten into joints and other planes of weakness and together with subaerial weathering has produced curious features resembling great blocks roughly piled upon one another. Their surfaces are clean, but rough in detail owing to the differential rates of erosion of the various minerals of which the granite is composed. Sometimes the surface of the large blocks may be hollowed out into kettles and pans; in other places weathering and marine erosion may produce spiky forms. Often large slabs are left projecting or overhanging. In the lower parts where the cliffs, in the ordinary sense of the word, are insignificant or even absent, the outlines may be most irregular. The granite readily breaks down into sand, and bayhead beaches and tombolos are common. There are also cracks, running generally a little west of north. These are most conspicuous on the northern shores, where the Atlantic waves eat out the crushed granite along them. There is reason for thinking that these cracks are a result of the latest movements which have affected the granite, but they definitely have a great influence on the configuration of the islands as a whole, and of the waterways leading to the Interior sea.

In some islands, especially in Great Ganilly, there is a series of vertical cracks along which there has been some alteration of the granite. These cracks are often referred to as Greisen[1] lines. They are also easily eroded by the sea, which has locally cut deep inlets along them. An example occurs at the south end of White Island (St. Martin's); the inlet is extremely like a geo. On a bigger scale the effect of erosion along these lines is seen in the long inlets near Old Town, St. Mary's.

[1] Greisening, see note, page 244.

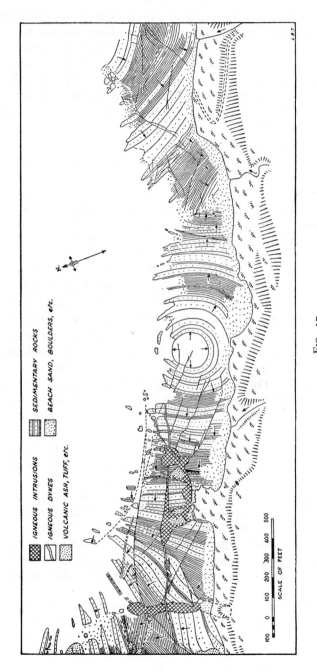

FIG. 17

Coast platform showing Sedimentary Structures and Igneous necks between Kinkell Ness and Kingask, Fifeshire. (After S. R. Kirk)

There is another good stretch of granite coast on either side of Peterhead, in Aberdeenshire. The country within is for the most part a plateau some 100-200 feet high. The cliffs are steep and picturesque. Locally they have been modified by quarrying. Lines of weakness are picked out by the waves, but castellated forms are not conspicuous. The area is perhaps of greater interest as a contrast to Land's End and the Scillies. At the present time, although wave action is at times considerable, it is hardly comparable to the almost constant attack of the Atlantic. A small but interesting mass of granite forms part of the west coast of the isle of Rum. The rock is whitish-grey in colour, and presents bold and wild scenery. Great screes descend the seaward slopes, which, however, do not reach to sea level. All along this part of the island there is a well-marked raised rock platform, which is the more interesting because this is an exposed coast and directly open to the south-west ocean between the southern end of The Long Island and the north of Tiree and Coll. Yet modern erosion is doing no more than cutting into a platform produced earlier (Pl. 4b, p. 184).

Between St. Andrews and the neighbourhood of Dunbar the local stratified rocks, mainly limestones, shales, and sandstones of the Calciferous Sandstone series, are pierced by a large number of old volcanic vents. Originally these vents were the feeding pipes of small volcanoes of the nature of Largo Law, Kellie Law, Traprain Law, and others. They have suffered much from subaerial denudation, and nowadays only the plugs remain. The coastal examples are usually on a small scale, and often the sea has cut through them so that they may scarcely affect the general height of the wave-cut platform. In other places the harder masses of tuff, agglomerate, or lava form irregular stacks and produce considerable local detail. In addition to the vents or necks, there are many dykes and sills which can be seen in plan on the beach platform and in section in the cliffs.

To understand something of the general appearance of these igneous features it is important to realise that along many parts of the coast of the Firth of Forth there is a good rock-cut bench. As seen from the cliffs the sedimentary structures are sometimes beautifully displayed (see Fig. 17)—synclines, domes, and anticlines, very often cut by faults. It is through this platform that the necks have burst.

Tuff and agglomerate by their very nature form irregular cliffs especially in detail. Usually the matrix of the tuff yields more easily to erosion than do the harder boulders enclosed in it, which project

Plate Va OLD RED SANDSTONE CLIFFS: the Old Red Sandstone makes magnificent cliffs, the form of which varies with differences in the rock and in inclination of the beds. This picture shows horizontally and fairly thinly bedded rocks forming vertical cliffs on the Caithness coast near Ires Geo

b CROVIE, GARDENSTOWN AND PENNAN are three small fishing villages built at the foot of north-facing cliffs in Banffshire and Aberdeenshire. As the picture shows, Gardenstown is subject to erosion

J. A. Steers

Plate VI GREAT ORME'S HEAD: this conspicuous headland on the coast of North Wales is formed of Carboniferous Limestone. It is joined to the mainland by an isthmus of blown sand

(Aerofilms, Ltd.)

as knobs and crags, both in the beach platform and, if conditions are suitable, in the cliffs also. Dykes cutting through this kind of material usually stand out as wall-like masses, or, at a rather later stage, form stacks. One of the finest and best-known examples is that called the Rock and Spindle, a mile or two south of St. Andrews. This is part of an irregularly shaped vent, and at its northern end there is a detached mass indicating a separate orifice. The greatest diameter is about 280 yards. The vent, like others hereabouts, has been drilled through the Calciferous Sandstone series, and masses, large and small, of these rocks together with tuff and agglomerate, are found in the vent. Sometimes a rough stratification is noticeable, resulting from rapid lens-shaped alternations of coarse and fine debris. The whole arrangement suggests an intermittently active cone, that usually ejected dust and fine material but every now and again threw up much larger masses of basalt. The rocks through which the neck cuts are highly inclined.

The neck is intersected by many basaltic intrusions, and since one series of intrusions cuts across another they are clearly of two distinct ages. The older material is dull green in colour and some of it forms the stack which is called the Rock[1] and Spindle. The other material is less decomposed, and usually occurs in more regular dykes, one of which cuts the Rock and Spindle. The Spindle is composed of basalt which must have been injected into a large cavity; the result has been that its columns radiate like the spokes of a wheel. In other words, they have formed at right angles to the cooling surface. The stack is well known, and was first described by Lyell in his *Elements of Geology*. In part of the same vent is another lumpy stack of the more formless type so often associated with these vents.

Another striking example occurs at Kincraig Hill to the west of Elie. The cliffs reach about 200 feet in height and are steep or even precipitous. They are fronted by a shore platform which is cut in agglomerate, and is much roughened by knobs, crags, stacks, gullies, and holes cut by the waves. The cliff itself is made up mainly of tuff and agglomerate, but locally the basalt which occupies the central part of the neck shows excellent columnar structure. This is a far bigger neck than that of the Rock and Spindle; and part of it is still beneath the sea or hidden under superficial deposits. It has been estimated that the east-west axis must measure at least one mile, and that from north to south half a mile. Once again the neck ascends

[1] The word rock is the Scots word for distaff.

through highly inclined sediments, and consists of ordinary volcanic detritus, bombs, dykes, blocks of country rock, and a matrix of finer material.

Some of these necks are very small. At Newark there is a miniature but perfect example which has been beautifully exposed by marine erosion. It measures 60 by 37 yards. The material in it is mainly agglomerate formed of local rocks and bedded in the usual green tuff of the Fifeshire volcanic district. Figure 18 shows that it cuts through

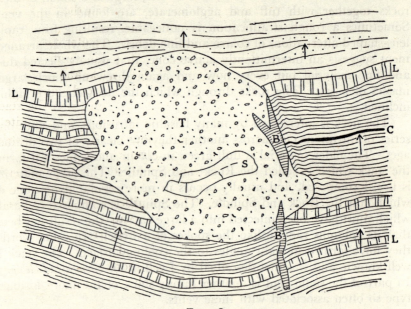

FIG. 18

Newark Dovecot Vent. (After Sir A. Geikie)

T, Agglomerate of Neck; S, Block of Sandstone in Agglomerate; B, Basalt Vents; L, Beds of limestone and cement stone; C, Thin coal seam in black shales. Arrows show dip of surrounding strata

rocks having a noticeable dip, and that in the neck itself are basalt veins and a large block of sandstone.

There is no need to describe more of these vents on the Fifeshire side of the Firth, but a word is desirable about the general nature of those on the south side. There are many examples which are easily examined between North Berwick and Dunbar. The Leithes (North Berwick) consist of several basaltic masses rising above the green ashes of the shore. The whole complex makes a small rocky promontory which is tied by a sandbank to the mainland at low water, and becomes eight separate rocks or islets at high water. At the Horseshoe vent a very large bomb in the agglomerate forms a miniature stack. Tantallon Castle stands on a great cliff of agglomerate inside the vent of the same name, and a fault in the agglomerate gives rise to a deep glen in the cliff. Farther east, at Whitberry Vent (St. Baldred's), the intrusive basalt is nearly circular in plan, and on its seaward side forms low cliffs showing good jointing and columnar structure. A large indentation is called St. Baldred's Cradle. At Dunbar the castle stands on part of an old vent.

It is almost supererogatory to emphasise the irregular nature of the shores associated with these necks. Local metamorphism has often toughened the rocks immediately surrounding a neck, and the varying hardnesses of the material in the vents have produced minor stacks. These are nearly always formless and differ greatly from the stacks associated with ordinary stratified rocks or with masses of granite or basalt. Moreover, the dull green-black colour makes them somewhat unattractive. Nevertheless they form a distinct category, and their unusual forms, their localised nature, and sombre colouring are characteristic.

A few only of the vents have been described, although there is a considerable number of them. Some stand isolated, others are in close conjunction one with another. It is partly their irregular occurrence and partly the extremely mixed and disturbed rocks in and around each that gives such heterogeneity to these shores. What these vents were like when they were formed, probably in Permian times, can only be conjectured. Presumably they formed small ash cones with solid cores, like those (cores) that still remain in Largo Law, Kellie Law, and other inland hills. Marine erosion working on the assortment of materials found in the coastal vents has produced the features we see today.

THE OLD RED SANDSTONE AND COASTAL SCENERY

It might be worth while debating which of our stratified rocks forms the finest coastal scenery. Strong views would undoubtedly be expressed, and there would certainly be much support for the Old Red Sandstone. This formation, as far as coastal scenery is concerned, is best developed in Scotland. In Caithness and between Stonehaven and Arbroath there are some remarkably fine lines of cliffs and excellent coastal detail associated with them.[1]

The interior of Caithness is a rolling plateau, sometimes falling to sea level as in Sinclair's Bay and Dunnett Bay, but elsewhere facing the sea in long lines of cliffs like those between Noss Head and Dunbeath, those in the Duncansby district, and those at Dunnett Head and west from Holborn Head. The Old Red Sandstone varies a good deal in its composition; it may be conglomeratic and arranged in thick beds as in the massive cliffs and stacks between Ulbster and Sarclet, or it may occur in the form of flagstones as at Duncansby and Dunnett. In general the rocks are not greatly disturbed and face the sea with horizontal or but slightly inclined bedding. They are also well jointed at right angles to the bedding. Hence the sea eats in along these lines of weakness and produces caves, recesses, buttresses, and stacks. But nearly everywhere the material of the stacks and cliffs is hard and resistant, so that although the sea continues to penetrate in the joints and other lines of weakness, the wearing away of the intervening parts is a slow process. Where the material which forms the cliffs is more heterogeneous, the conglomerates stand out from the softer sandstones. Some of the finest stacks in Great Britain are close to Duncansby Head. They rise from a narrow platform of marine erosion, probably produced when the sea was cutting the low (5 foot) raised beach occasionally seen in Caithness. That this is a slightly raised feature is also suggested strongly by the presence of a narrow beach of lichen-covered boulders near Duncansby. The stacks are high and form great pinnacles. The bedding is conspicuous, and their rather irregular form results from the varying hardness of the beds composing them. They are formed in flagstones, which are hard and tough. Their grain is fine, and since even the smallest pores are infilled with lime, the rocks as a whole are to all intents and purposes air-and water-tight. " The limitation of decay to exposed surfaces, and easy removal of the weathered crust are the main peculiarities in their weathering, but the different laminae are unequally affected. . . . The cemented nature of the rocks causes them to react in bulk to tensile forces, and vertical joint-planes are of great depth and form the chief structural lines of weakness. . . . These vertical planes form the only channels through which water can easily percolate the rock masses. The joint-planes cross one another in the direction of the dip and strike of the strata, and map out the flag-

[1] See also pages 92 and 195.

stones into blocks of a more or less rectangular shape. . . . The planes
of bedding, though so well marked, are, except in disturbed areas,
hermetically sealed against percolating waters. . . . When in a horizontal position and little jointed, the flagstones are almost unassailable

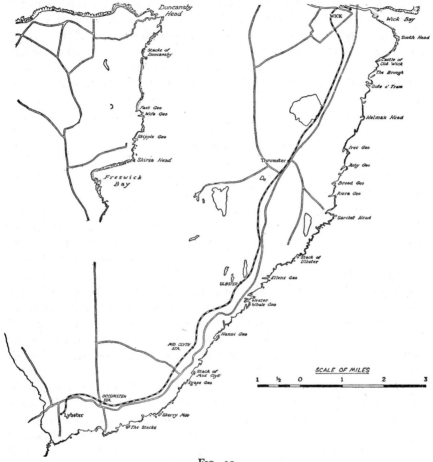

FIG. 19

Part of the Coast of Caithness

and their strength is frequently demonstrated by the natural tables,
bridges, and arches which ornament the coast."[1]

When the strike is roughly parallel to the coast, reefs are formed,

[1] *Mems. Geol. Surv. Scotland*, The Geology of Caithness, C. B. Crampton and
R. G. Carruthers, 1914, p. 162.

but when it runs at a high angle to the line of cliffs, skerries occur. The best detail is usually found where the cliffs are high and the bedding more or less horizontal. In such places long, narrow inlets (geos) are cut by wave action along lines of weakness—for the most part major joint planes (Fig. 19). These inlets have steep, parallel, walls which are often vertical. At their upper ends they may show either a talus slope indicating that erosion has ceased, or a cave, implying that erosion is still active. If the dip of the rocks is fairly high, geos may still be present but more irregular in form and commonly less profound. At Holborn Head, crushes are sometimes present in the rocks, and if suitably situated relative to sea level, caves and undermining by the sea result. These in their turn may lead to the formation of blowholes. Around the top of these holes, even on high cliffs, there is nearly always a scatter of pebbles, some quite large, which have been blown up during a storm. In other places (there is a good example near Nybster) undermining has caused the coast to subside along a line roughly parallel with the cliff edge.

The cutting of stacks and arches may be a fairly rapid process, but their subsequent destruction occupies a long time. They are of all sizes. The bigger ones, called Cletts, are 20 or 30 or more yards across; that at Holborn Head is a fine example. Many of the Caithness stacks still retain a covering of boulder clay or even peat, and are locally the haunt of numerous sea birds. Some large stacks are undermined by caves and arches, and eventually resemble massive tables supported on legs, like the Brough, about two miles south of Wick. The stacks are nearly always within about 100 yards of the cliffs; it is uncertain if this distance measures only recent erosion or erosion over a longer period.

North of Arbroath there is another fine stretch of Old Red Sandstone cliffs. For a mile or more north of Whiting Ness the cliffs show admirable detail. They are less high than those at Duncansby, but they are cut by gullies which resemble the geos of Caithness. Hickling[1] has suggested that these originate as caves, of which there are several examples. It is not unlikely, however, that since they are cut along major joints, they have always been open to the sky. Blowholes are also formed; one known as the Mermaids' Kirk and another at the entrance of Dickmouth Glen are good examples. We are, however, not dealing only with present-day erosion. The stack known as the Deil's Head cannot have been formed today, but at a time when the

[1] *Proc. Geol. Assoc.*, 23, 1912, 302.

land stood, relative to the sea, at a lower level. What is of further interest concerning this stack is the fact that the master joint which allowed its severance continues southward through a cliff spur, and the stack called the Three Storey House is now in process of formation, entirely as a result of existing conditions. Up to this point the coast has coincided with the strike of the rocks. Since there is a fairly steady dip to the south-east at 20°–25°, the cliff profile is not particularly bold, and is partly fronted by a platform cut when the levels of land and sea were different. Carlingheugh Bay is carved out of the relatively softer Upper Old Red Sandstone, which here consists largely of alternations of conglomerates with soft, false-bedded, and rather light-coloured sandstones. The bedding is nearly horizontal, and in the bay are extensive ledges of rock (the Floors) running nearly 300 yards out to sea. Since they are just awash at high water, there is little doubt that they are the remnants of a raised beach platform.

Similar features, varying locally with the nature of the rock, the dip, and minor faulting continue as far north as Lunan Bay. Unfortunately, there is no space to describe all parts of the Old Red Sandstone coast, but special mention must be made of the fine cliffs and geos between Catterline and Stonehaven, the geo and waterfall at Crawton, and the intricate series of islets just south of and at Dunnottar Castle. The castle itself stands on a great stack or clett.

All types of coastline possess great attraction, but a walk along cliffs of Old Red Sandstone is a memorable experience. There is so much variety of detail and so much colour in the cliffs themselves that it is impossible to go more than a hundred yards or so without stopping to contemplate the scenery and to speculate on the processes of its evolution. Although the rocks are similar in Kincardine and Caithness, their details and setting are different. The high cliffs and magnificent stacks of Duncansby, the precipices of Dunnet Head, or the range of vertical, even overhanging, cliffs west of Holborn Head, are different from the intricately moulded but less exposed coast north of Arbroath. Moreover, the agricultural land on the cliff tops of Kincardine stands in sharp contrast to the cotton grass moor or turf-covered moorlands of Caithness.

But both areas are unlike the Old Red Sandstone in Pembrokeshire. Near St. Bride's, on the south shore of the bay of the same name, the formation occurs locally and forms fine brightly coloured cliffs which are sharply distinguished from the other rocks, as seen, for example, in Musselwick Bay. But it is in the peninsula south of

Milford Haven that the Old Red Sandstone shows to great advantage. This is an area of Armorican folding (see page 7), and the Old Red Sandstone is no longer horizontal, or nearly so, as it is in the areas discussed in Scotland. Cliffs of this series appear in both Freshwater West and Freshwater East Bays. Between Freshwater East and Old Castle Head the strata are almost on end, and the strike is nearly parallel to the coast. The cliffs are not particularly bold, and seen from above the arrangement of the rocks gives a striped effect, especially where beds of different colours (for the most part red and grey-green) outcrop. There are no geos along this coast, but inlets or bays like Precipe, Manorbier, and Swanlake are due largely, if not wholly, to marine erosion acting along groups of small faults.

LIMESTONE COASTS

In all sedimentary rocks, the shape of the cliff depends largely on details of bedding, dip, and strike, and the way the rocks actually occur on the coast. The factor peculiar to limestones is their solubility. While, however, solution by marine waters may play some part, it is that of surface waters, either in the past or in the present, that is often the more important.

Perhaps the finest example of a limestone coast in Great Britain is that formed by the Carboniferous Limestone in the Tenby peninsula of Wales. The surface of the limestone is a level plateau about 100 to 160 feet high. The cliffs cut in it are nearly vertical, and locally project as conspicuous promontories, e.g. St. Gowan's Head and Stackpole Head. The rock is well bedded and jointed. Sometimes the bedding is massive, at other times thin. There is a marked absence of sand and clay. Many of the more interesting details, especially those in Bullslaughter Bay, are the result of the sea cutting back into ramifying caves and grottoes formed at an earlier time by the solvent action of surface waters. Stacks and arches, caves, cauldrons, and blowholes, are all common. At St. Gowan's Head the limestones are thick bedded and gently folded, and since they are also rectangularly jointed they form precipices. At the well-known Green Bridge of Wales, the arch is formed of massive limestones, whilst the hollow is cut in thinner beds. The buttress is carved along joint planes, and its farther end, seaward of the bridge, is now cut off and remains as a low stack. At Eligug the sea has cut through a spur of massive limestones, and by working along joints has made gaps and so reduced